A RAY OF D

A
RAY OF DARKNESS

BY

MARGIAD EVANS

JOHN CALDER · LONDON

RIVERRUN PRESS · DALLAS

Originally published in 1952 by
Arthur Barker Ltd, 21 Garrick Street,
Covent Garden, London
This new edition first published 1978 in Great Britain by
John Calder (Publishers) Ltd,
18 Brewer Street, London W1R 4AS
and in the USA by Riverrun Press Inc.
4951 Top Line Drive, Dallas Texas 75247
© Mrs. C. E. Davis 1952, 1978

ISBN 0 7145 3727 6 casebound
ISBN 0 7145 3607 5 paperbound

The publishers gratefully acknowledge financial support from the
English Language Section of Yr Academi Gymreig.

Printed in Great Britain by
M. & A. Thomson Litho Ltd, East Kilbride, Scotland
Bound in Great Britain by
Hunter & Foulis Ltd, Edinburgh, Scotland

There is in God (some say)
a deep but dazzling darkness . . .
          HENRY VAUGHAN, *The Night*

But for the night I had forgot my goal;
but for the night the single light had lost;
but for the night recovered not day's cost,

Chosen not out my wish where beams unroll
a universe desired from pole to pole:
shapeless with width and hampered with the host
of hopes superfluous and joys that tossed
their glitter like the lustre of a goal.
          MARGIAD EVANS, *The Guide Invisible*

PART I

CHAPTER I

ALL people afflicted with neurosis, neurotic tendencies, diseases or threats of diseases of the brain or mind seem to write a great many letters, which bore their families and friends. It is not remarkable for the letters are usually badly and chaotically written, mis-spelt and extremely long. They are, as I was told by one person who had suffered from mine, garrulous. Undoubtedly the possession of a serious illness causes a morbid sort of pride: but there is also a passionate yearning, as one retreats further and further from their understanding, to be understood by ordinary and well people. But it is not reciprocated. Mr. John Custance says in his recent book *Wisdom, Madness and Folly:*

'I cannot, however hard I try, get even my most intimate relatives and friends to understand or take any interest in what may or may not have happened to me during my "madness." Gradually the vividness of my memory fades; like my relatives, I try to put the whole experience out of my mind, and in fact it does to a certain extent disappear into the lower levels of my Unconscious.'

This is exactly what I, as a sufferer from epilepsy, have experienced, including both the outside treatment and the *inner forgetfulness,* providing the interval between the fits is long enough to forget in. Which is not always so, and anyway I no longer desire to put out of my mind what my mind has received. My mood, after rather more than a year of major epilepsy, is to accept and not to reject the experience.

Mr. Custance is a manic-depressive and a learned philosopher. He has been ill much longer than I and has read much more. I am a woman of forty-two. Technically knowing nothing of philosophy and nothing of psychology. That is no more than any writer who has observed people and tried to create them. For I have been a novelist and still write poetry and keep notes and diaries when there is time. For my first child, a daughter called Cassandra, was born three months ago. This longing to write of one's symptoms appears like an inspiration to write a great story. Cut off from mentioning my fits in conversation or in letters, I resolved that I would write the plain narrative as a book. Perhaps the urge is curative and people turn to it as a dog eats grass? I don't know—I know nothing except that I have felt and ceased to feel, lived and while living, ceased to live. Certainly I could not pretend there was any moral or philosophical value in this book. I have had nothing to teach from my epilepsy: I do not know that I even believe in what is called 'the value of experience.' People speak often of having benefited, having learned a lot, by coming into contact with this and that. Learned what? By learned do they mean merely heard about? To hear about seems to me to be the modern equivalent for learning.

To hear of or to hear about. And afterwards what more?

To *learn* is surely to absorb, to grow out of something absorbed, as plants grow out of sunlight and dew. If I have learned anything from being epileptic it is only a closer knowledge of the symptoms which I had watched before in dogs very, very often, what sudden and utter unconsciousness is like when *it happens* to oneself. The experience of watching turned inside out is the experience of Being or Having.

Epilepsy was called once Possession. (And once I thought it was the Muse herself in rage turning on one who had neglected her for years of common tasks and common existence.) *Possession* it may be. But it is the Possession by the sufferer of epilepsy, not his by the seizure. It is, like Mr. Custance's insanity, to be treasured and, if the cure should ever come, to be remembered. For one thing unconsciousness *can* teach. It can gently, and as it were, by steps or a staircase, show us the probable darkness of death, and remove our fear of that descent. I know there is nothing to fear in death now, except possibly the instant before it takes place, when the event races, or almost races, the tremor of terror to the spirit. That I have learned, and that to the few who fear death I would re-write and re-emphasize. Do not be afraid. There is no fear of Death. There can be no fear where oblivion is ahead of sensation.

But if there is nothing to be learned in the literal sense from illness, nothing to be taught or inferred, there is, as any conversation overheard in bus or train, very much to be enjoyed. If not at the time, later, and if not by ourselves by others. Symptoms are as interesting as politics or the weather; they are a continuous story, an adventure serial where the end, if not happy, is definite. Our health is as a voyage: and every illness is an adventure story. The leader of the adventure is the doctor: think of him as the Captain if you wish, while the patient is vessel, crew and passenger all in one. The Captain, trained in navigation, foresees the dangers and pains of the ocean, the passenger, like Melville's Ishmael in the crow's nest, looks out on the wondrous Pacific calms, the deeps and the waves he must sail without head knowledge. For in disease there *are* wondrous calms and profound lulls: there are thoughts and contemplations of which no other deeps can give us hints, and the voyage, to the sufferer, may even be beautiful though he never again see land and home. Or such land and such home as he is used to calling land and home.

The story of my epilepsy then is given here as an adventure of body and mind. The telling is as simple as I can make it and ignorance of medical terms can keep it. There is no teaching, no philosophy and no comfort intended in it. It is the truth, most of it exactly as it was written down at the time, for I have my diaries.

CHAPTER II

Oh Death, how rare complete
with grief and mourning!

THERE are, I have been told on the highest authority,[1] about seventy different causes of epilepsy. One must be careful, therefore, before naming oneself or any one else an epileptic. For epilepsy is a symptom rather than a complete disease. Nevertheless, a certain peculiar temperament would appear to go with the symptoms of epileptic fits. In the application form sent out to my husband, a teacher, to be filled in if he wished to take up work in an epileptic colony's school, this temperament was briefly indicated. I must say that it coincided with many of the defects as well as the talents which I know I possess. The children are described as maladjusted and prone to brood on real or fancied wrongs. I was a child who felt I was deprived of something which I cannot define, but something longed for, something half divine, perhaps, between love and liberty. At the same time I have always had long or short spells of profound harmony and peace which righted the agonies, the hatreds and the unreturned loves of my youth. This harmony and peace came directly from nature and landscape: not until I was within two years of my first fit did I associate it with God.[2] Certainly I have no other religion except the enjoyment of nature and the belief that all life should be treated with

[1] Professor T—— of the Neurological Institute, Clystow.
[2] In *Autobiography* I have described this sense of communion.

13

tenderness. (This last clause seems to me to be the germ of all Dostoëffsky's work.) But mine is not a serious case. It is major epilepsy, but thanks to my doctor, to Professor T—— and to the drugs they prescribe and regulate for me, the attacks are not frequent. If they were, I could be insane, for within each seizure is embedded an embryonic second of such terror that body and mind recoil from any association with it.

For two reasons then I cannot call myself *an epileptic*. But in reading Mr. Custance's descriptions of manic-depression I have found affinities with the epileptic character. The periods of heated expansion or inspiration, and those of cold contraction and uninspired misery, compare with my own memories, though mine are, of course, much slighter with less comparison and opposition (opposite-ness?). The inspiration is not to be trusted: creatively I have worked best when most steadily; that is when writing through all moods. For the past two years I have written scarcely anything more than diaries and notes, an odd lyric occasionally, and one long essay on childhood. I have abandoned a book I began on Emily Brontë because the mysterious and isolated figure of the self-martyred poet was expanding over all the creative figures of literary or thoughtful or poetic greatness who came into my mind: and was conversely absorbing the universe as I can conceive it. The book as contemplated was nearer to madness than I could face. I abandoned it soon after my first attack in May 1950. Objective writing, except of a very simple descriptive kind (trees, storms, woods, bird-life), was impossible to me. The farthest figures of grandeur I knew of seemed to be becoming a part of *my* life and thought. The God Apollo and the divine genius Bach I mention as two of the images which dominated me at different times during the last few years.[1] The last few free years! Free of disease, free of family, a wonderful, magnificent and perpetual youth held me, as soon as I left the homes where we lived and stepped into the grass or the snow. But that something wrong, dangerous, *different* was imminent part of me sensed. I should like to give a short description of this condition which lasted for some three years and culminated in my first fit.

In *Autobiography* there was religion but it was religion incomplete, it was the worship of nature and solitude, the worship perhaps of God's body and not the soul of God. That was written about ten years ago. As time passed and I was always surrounded with beauty, the religious feeling grew, I think, and I meditated more and more often on it. What is religion? I asked myself (for being an egotistical-epileptic I would never ask any other authority). What is religion? It is reverence, tenderness, love, joy and worship. Reverence, tenderness, love and worship I could have given to another human being; but not joy. There was this deep religious sense in me, but nothing on which to pour it out. No person and no faith fits it; therefore it may perhaps have been created by God to be given back to him? I read the Old Testament—the New I could never

[1] The God Apollo, God of light, God of medicine and wisdom, intuition and music, was with me during the whole of one summer three years ago. Particularly he seemed to be associated with *honeysuckle* which I would touch by the brook where it grew wild but never pick.

Bach I have always worshipped. His music causes the hwl in my heart (the hwl is the chant of passion in Welsh preaching—the carrying away of the voice on the spirit of ardour) both for its sound and its construction.

Another figure which dominated my imagination was the great and tragic personality of Jacob Stainer, the 17th century Liutaro (a maker of stringed instruments). I have written poems to all these godheads of my ideals. In the essay 'The Man with the Hammer' printed in *Life and Letters*, I gave a short biography of Stainer. He was often insane, and the bench to which he was tied during his spells of madness is, or was until lately, in existence. His violins are, I think, the most beautiful in form of all, not excepting Stradivari's.

like. In Lamentations there is a verse which used to make me weep: "For he doth not willingly afflict."

I was very busy—there was much to be done for I like cleanliness indoors, and there was the garden; gradually a most disagreeable and threatening sort of restlessness spoiled all my happiness and took away my peace. It is hard to describe, but it was as though I couldn't stop *hurrying*. I lingered over nothing, neither work nor loveliness. As soon as I began a thing I longed for it to be over; and my smallest jobs I could see and count ahead of me in an endless line. I hurried to get them done and when they were done I had no spirit in me to enjoy the time saved by the haste. Precious sights slipped past me: one short gaze at a lovely thing, the moon or the evening star over the fields, or a flower or the face of my really beloved old neighbour, and I would shoot away to something else. Thus concentration began to slip: and in my writing I, who had always written so thoughtfully and so slowly that words and phrases were like a birth, began to race over the pages without stopping. In a sense I wrote more easily; and what was remarkable lyric poems of some real beauty began to come from me, who had never written any passable poetry. My prose deteriorated into a scurry and a tediousness, but my poetry began to separate itself, and I loved it far the better of the two. And why not? The precision of the medium gives it the power to concentrate and to form the idea far more accurately than prose, which, though easier to write, is too pliant. To incorporate a thought in prose is like trying to model a figure in slack clay instead of poetry's stone. During the last years before the fits I wrote practically nothing but poetry—it was my reading also. The poets I chose were Wordsworth, George Herbert, Henry Vaughan, Walter Raleigh, King David and Milton.

I was unhappy and uneasy and incessant but never bored except with people, and most bored of all if I had to listen to any one talking for long or addressing a crowd.

I am strong and had no fears about my health. This horrible hurry, which I am sure now was in my brain, seemed to me just a part of middle age, poverty and doing your own work.

At this stage, two and a half years ago, our cottage was sold over us, the farm changed hands and my husband left work on the land to take up teaching. I went to live at St. Ides, close to where we were born, with my sister who had only just moved there herself. So terrified and bewildered were my husband and I at our separation from each other and our lovely county (Herefordshire) that he lost his head one day and had a dog we both adored put down. It was the puppy of my dear spaniel Rosie. It had a bad effect on *him*; on me it was terrific. I grieved and grieved. I used to look up at a certain constellation and fancy I saw the shape of Dobie hanging there watching me. All seemed gone from me—the miles of green beauty changed for suburbia, Nature straitened and starved, a few orchards, a few poor-looking fields. Those fields, how I came to adore them, how I will always remember them, for from them Nature seemed to put out itself and grip me back to itself as I was dissolving into desolation. In a dell, under some trees where my mother, whom I love dearly, had played as a child—an unhappy child—I found that spring some white violets; and in my spirit cried articulately, 'They are here, they are here too—Nature is here—there is life enough for the heart.' And as the grass grew and the hedges bloomed, my terrible grief recovered. Or began to recover.

But grief is never unlearned. My entranced youth was

over, prolonged as it had been beyond youth by feeling through the imperishable earth. I wrote until early mornings in my bedroom, listening to the sound of the pine trees above my room whose shadow it seemed I could hear in the dark. And my poems were all on death, were all requiems. Derek Savage, in his survey of the modern novel *The Withered Branch*, said he had discovered 'the death wish' in my work written years before. I had never felt it until then, in fact I do not think it was in truth present before.

CHAPTER III

"A long war disturbed your mind;
here your perfect peace is signed."

Webster

(from *The Duchess of Malfi*)

My nights are my greatest loss. For since taking drugs I
cannot keep awake for those free quiet hours which were
my most creative. True my power of concentration is
lost also; but part of the badness of my prose here and
elsewhere is due to writing in snatched moments instead
of long freedom when the dark calm hours stretched
before me like great empty pages: on which, my labours
finished, I could sleep and afterwards could regard as the
paragraphs of my conscious meditations.

It has been necessary to cut the foregoing chapter into
two pieces. This is my 'short description'! And this is
typical of my position in thought to-day. It is all too long,
too 'garrulous.' Is it symptomatic of epilepsy that the mind
seems to expand in all directions at once? I believe that it
is; and this explains the intricate style of all epileptic people
who have written; for example, the universality of
Dostoëffsky, so noble, so interesting and so hard to follow
as opposed to the universality of Tolstoi, where the same
vast and gentle outlook is ordered to a beautiful coherence,
an exact sequence.

It takes such a lot to fill the human mind! Even the
ordinary mind, on which Proust and James Joyce laboured
for all their lives. I had reached Death and the Death wish

in the last pages. It was not that I wished to die but that the thought of death to my hurried, anxious mind was lovely and soothing. To return to Earth and to lie still with no labours unfinished sounding their dissonance for ever in my spirit. Such a conception of dying seemed not at variance with my older desire for old age with which I also associated peace and climax; nor with the mysterious earth love which was then and now my only consistent solace. I would think of it as I lay awake after reading the psalms or George Herbert or Vaughan during those night hours when my brain had danced itself to exhaustion on the pages before me. I would think of it even in the moment of supreme life which I felt I shared with the spring, when I saw the cherry orchards in bloom, when I touched the face of a hedge rose or felt the summer grasses stroke my bare legs as I walked through the fields. It was death and life together because in my brain all opposites were being reconciled with one another, and all the world and myself becoming more and more to each other, while I was more and more of the natural Oneness I had sensed all my life and had tried so often to convey in *Autobiography*. It was as near the achievement of the mystic state as I was ever to attain.

In connection with opposites becoming sympathetic while a mysterious sense of harmony prevails, I must mention my belief that the value of this condition of mind is solely dependent upon the everydayness of the mind which is experiencing it. It is not in moments of mystic or sensory exultation and excitement we must trust to this intimation of God's unity with us, but in moments of commonness and ordinary life. It is for this reason I distrust most of the Saints and the faiths they have impersonated while feeling that Emily Brontë can safely be scrutinized.

(It will be remembered that in her last hours she fed her dog, and in her last weeks did her housework.)

I do not idealize Emily Brontë as so many death-mystics incline to do. In my study of her, my sympathies went of their own accord to her sister Charlotte, and my respect to the heroic Anne. But when I tried to write of them, the distinctions faded and I found the three sisters merging into one personality—another example of the Oneness which Mr. John Custance describes as one of the experiences of his manic-depression.

What was my physical health at this time? It was abounding—except for very bad, dull headaches which I put down to rheumatism. They came two or three times a week, preventing me from thinking or enjoying anything. They were annoying but one thinks nothing of headaches when one has been told that one has rheumatic nodules at the back of the neck. There was, however, another strange symptom which I wonder now did not attract my attention. This was a peculiar giddiness which I have had only three or four times since my fits began, but which came then very often. Every time I had it I used to think of bowling and the biassed 'woods,' for it was not that the solid world appeared to move around me as in ordinary giddiness, but that in a steady world my head felt awry. It was, in short, as if my brain inside my skull was askew or weighted at one side. It was disagreeable: I used to get up with it and it usually lasted until nightfall.

As the summer grew I came to love this place where I had been a child more and more; and I also lost a great deal of my intense unhappiness, for my younger sister and myself have always been happy together and I deeply loved her little boy who was then two years old and had given me a name he had made for me himself. Yet in the midst of joy, my preoccupation with death remained. Death, which symbolized peace and natural growth. Here are some poems I wrote which were printed in *Life and Letters*. It will be seen that I felt my life would not be a long one, as I feel now. That is why I never forget time passing, time coming up behind and passing me, like Andrew Marvell. No more than if my brain were a clock face can it cease for one moment to register the race.

Two of these poems appeared last year, but their date is the summer I am describing, 1949.

Traveller's Joy

If they should ask you where I am
say, she is travelling in the grave,
pleased to be absent from her tiring home
and holiday from light awhile to have.

Absence is Presence altered: so disguised
I range beyond the deserts and the sea:
Absence is Presence changed, and so revised
within the empty mirror look at me.

Tell them, the journey is but temporary,
the roots are million that return,
a thoughtful eye on Nature's constancy
is bound to meet me often coming home.

The clue to this poem, every word of which meant much to me and was as exact as I could make it, was the word *roots*, 'the roots are million that return.' The poem is a statement of my conviction that my being and all natural life were in substance and spirit, one, and that in one form or another, life lives on. It is not a particular requiem like some which followed it. This unity, or Oneness, experienced by Mr. Custance, by many lunatics, by mystics, with the Universe I believe to be only the first stage of God's appearance to the sufferer. All mystics begin as Nature mystics. Some, like Jefferies and Lawrence, stay there, but more go on, having begun, if they live.

It may seem absurd for an ordinary person suffering only slightly from intermittent epilepsy, to write so much at length about the state of mind before the fits began severely. I believe it is necessary to the understanding of the trouble— if trouble it is. Here is another poem of the same date written a night or two previously. In this poem the idea of Death as peace and rest is more clearly indicated.

The Will

Before I go I leave my Will and Testament
all that I have, apportioned to a day,
Figure by figure, name to name
written on parchment in the old manorial way.

To Stars, which are the Holy Families
I leave the praying habit of my eyes,
For there God took them—stoically inclined
his syllables in spacious brevities.

For Trees—my Edens—what have I enough
to sigh, to sign to them, but well rememberèd
(sweeping my mind!) the songs outlying winds
to islands in the blood have murmurèd.

A portion for a bird that sang
not insignificant, a love much worn
upon the centre of the heart
its kind, but not its lustrousness unknown.

My touch is for the flowers—they drew its nerves;
my hearing for the Music that makes lofty ears;
mountains take Resolution, prisons, Strength
that kept me from my personal fires.

Because it stilled the path for me
to grass I leave its own belovèd, Peace;
and to the sea, Eternal Being, briefly felt
as joy's, not life's increase.

Bequeath I to the sun my Hopes
to breed, a golden spread of sight;
yet gold untellable I take with me
to wall, to floor, to roof my coming night:

for with the gold I leave and take
much I may build of visions to entomb
Egyptian me, with seeds and weapons left
intact beneath an empty throne.

I remember how pleased I was at finding the word
'Egyptian' in my mind, with its associations with the long
quiet dead. Yet there is in 'seeds' and 'weapons' an idea
of a resurrection. I had, and perhaps still have, no faith
which will contain my worship of the earth; and I do not
think I believe in an Eternal separate identity of the soul.
Yet the sight of loveliness, the sound of Bach's music
would, each time, make even this for a little while possible.
And the greatness and goodness of some men. Who,
meeting a good man of whatever faith in God, has not felt
the Resurrection? And who of us has not, though he can
turn to no church, a priest in his heart?

To me, then, during this last summer before the dis-
location of my brain became apparent, the love of religion

was truly something 'its kind but not its lustrousness unknown.'

There are three more poems to quote in illustration of my preoccupation with the death theme, before I give some parts of my diary of that time and move on in my adventure story. The description of how I was the year before the strange voyage began, will then be complete. I was not happy, for I could never lose myself in timelessness as other happy people can, except late at night, when Time is drowned, clocks unwatched, the cockerel and his crow asleep.

Requiem I

Die? yes, I!
but what a mourning galaxy!
Earth's family
and cousins-in-the-light beside
me in the glistening avenues will ride.

Farewell green life,
farewell. Yet do not, eyes,
the lustre of the world with sadness dim.
What statelier fate
could Immortality create
or Prayer provide

than to be buried in your native star
with all of pompous space as sepulchre?

Requiem II

To go with song to funeral!
Happiness
is wordiness:

25

but Joy is silent as the Soul
and goes with stars to burial.

Requiem III

1

When voice no more can speak for me
and all my words are dead,
think how like day across your face
my love is spread.

2

The breath that made each thought distinct
is now a thing bequeathed,
like dew and essences of fields
the breezes breathed.

3

The last look she released on earth
still lives among the light,
but with the sun is travelling
towards the night.

4

No part that is not nature still
but natural for so short a time!
Until winds close and skies begin
their lofty lantern climb.

The epileptic person is an egotist, a supreme egotist but not by nature selfish. Nor without fortitude. If a person is born an egotist there is more to be received from him and more for him to give forth, than by trying to force him to a more general outlook. It is the same if he tries to alter himself. I do not believe that that quiet, proud, but humble egotism, which is content with domain among and over itself is bad, but the very reverse. Such natures are rich and original. Of them many may be quoted—notably Thoreau, whose powerful insistence on self-denial for self's sake so resembles the doctrine of heaven and hell. I am an egotist, but I have done my share or as much of my share as my physical strength would allow. I left no work undone for my writing and never had. I was an ordinary domestic woman by day, a poet or novelist or essayist by night. It was too much for me. The natural impulse to write *when* I wished for as long as I wished, might have caused the split which aggravated my tendency towards epilepsy. But the brain kept its secret still. Fortitude! Let any one try what tried me, day and night, the dual personality, the pressure of time, the headaches, dreams, etc., and they will guess the strength of my love for the fields and hedges which saved me for so long.

There is a still courage never known
except inwardly.
You would think it grew like grass
a marvellous monotony.

Some that were tender to themselves
once, now have it—brood
and live and live and live upon it
their hunger's plainest food.

There is a quiet habit—fields of it
that grows instead of battle, fury fire,
this is the existence of those grimmest pastures
no one thinks to plough.

There is a clench that dare not falter,
the heaviest branches' on the heaving tree,
that through all tempest makes its binding effort
to hold and hold indefinitely.

There is a human quality drains pale
the flesh that binds the muscular in soul;
no-one has heard the silent generations
through one in body endlessly unroll.

I ask you then when you go past someone
who to your gaze and hearing quietness gives,
the passionateness of Patience to remember,
and how Endurance lives.

I must pause here for balance to return. I was called
'placid' by many people in my thirties. I was told, 'you
look so happy.' No doubt it was true. The truth is God's.
I thank Him I *was* an egotist. How often in my pastoral
surroundings have I been told that there was no intellectual
life for me—I who had but to look at a leaf, to read a line
of poetry to myself, to feel the merging of all great imagery
into one enormous uncommunicable Art?

God is what prevents me
the Obstacle divine,

I wrote in my diary that summer, who was so soon
to feel the 'deep but dazzling darkness' of Vaughan's
imagination.

More than half of my journals then were in poetry. Life
had all gone, like blood, up to my head. On and on in
rhythm marched the two themes of kinship with Nature
and death.

28

Sleep

The sweetness of my opening days
would make my heart ache now
used to the silence of the night,
the bareness of the bough.
An hour in the dark holds more
discovery, than suns before.

It is not that life is the less,
nor daylight narrower, nor the bright hills
beheaded, fogged or lost; nor quiet
less deeply and less sweetly night time fills:
nor that *a sudden prophecy*
of ceasing, from oblivion rouses me.

It's not from grieving or despair
or fearfulness I wake to loneliness
and thought, but that my senses call
to me, and knowledge in my flesh
tells me with certainty how sleep's true place
is distanter than time or space.

Sleep has no home in earth and us
when we grow older, *nor has rest*
and when we sleep *it is a dream of sleep*
we taste, as love can dream the one it loves the best,
yet by its dreaming cannot stir
the loved one dead, or wearier.

Oh deep whole sleep! perfect, profound
lives not, is not, as once it was
inhabitor of me; but one forgotten year
left me and night with its uplifted pause,
to wait abroad like a disseevered star
a longer venture and a search more pure.

29

The italics are stresses not in the original, but put in by me now in illustration. Poetry is idealizing words: but I am not now using these verses as poems.

Happiness is divine.
But too much health is like too much light; it blinds.

CHAPTER IV

MIDSUMMER came—that ancient glow on the midyear when the Beltane was a festival. I remember midsummer night, how as it was getting dusk I was walking with the dogs in the meadows: and afterwards how at midnight I went down the path and stood under a tree alone, that the peak of the season's growth should not glide past me unwatched. Most of the trees were beeches there, whose fallen leaves in autumn crackle like shingle in the woods. This was an oak.

Mr. Custance speaks in his book *Wisdom, Madness and Folly* of the survival in us of primitive and primeval sensations and worships. It is one of his reiterated themes. Either this idea, not of course his own, is right: or we remain despite 'civilization' the same material to be affected in the same way by the spells or spokes of the turning skies. I can never allow the midsummer festival or the midwinter one to pass me unnoticed without disappointment. If I have, it is as though a musical string had slackened.

It was on Midsummer Eve I noticed how thickly the padded clover grew on the paths between the shorn grass. Here I wrote in my journal an entry which describes a happy and peaceful mental interlude.

Green Feet

Feet tread the vine
and through their tread we reach the wine.
Feet found first the generous lands
and gave them to the fertile hands.

31

Their tread is rich indeed;
for following their wise, observant speed,
I saw among the new cleared hay
how clover grows the thickest on a right-of-way.
They talk of green hands, but green feet
make barns and cattle cribs as sweet
in bitter January
as a flower's conservatory.
Peaceful the thought that greenest paths unwound
from ancient feet now dusty underground.

'Hotter than ever this afternoon. I made an expedition to St. Ides Le Poule and made the old Sexton tell me where the tap was for the dogs. Into the church for the first time. Some one had muttered to me something about murals: but here were not only murals but marvels. I could write a letter to myself about them: the three, related colours, the cave-like figure drawing, the lines, the bare and beautiful faces. A great artist made these heavenly drawings hundreds of years ago. I think them more beautiful than Blake's. Never have I seen so lovely a Salomé, conjuring with the dance. And the prophets and the Kings in Trees and the snake in Eden with an angel's face . . . I sat there in the cool, and outside the sunlight *buzzed* and the cows went to sleep in the hot fields. I felt enriched and satisfied this evening. I boiled the black-currant jam—five pounds of it—and as I sat and stirred, smelt their herb-like, leafy fragrance and saw outside the door, evening sunshine twisted about a cherry branch on which glowed the ripe, red drops of fruit. It did so fill my heart and eyes.'

Later there is a significant short entry: 'My head aches so dreadfully! In all the air there isn't a single soft place for it, nor has been all day.'

I watched the queer half-swift, half-torpid life of insects.

'Thou shalt hide them in the secret of thy Presence from the pride of man' (Psalm 31, verse 20).

I dreamed often of a cottage my husband and I were going to live in—a cottage I had never seen and of which there was no hope. Sometimes my little dead dog came into the dream, running down the stairs to greet me and licking me. About this time I had a dream which disturbed me very much, why I do not know. There was an old house in it, yellow brick with brown cracking lawns right up to the walls. This was the background. But close to me stood a short woman with a pale face and dark hair, wearing a queer three-quarter length grey cloak with a lot of folds.

'Have you any white wool?' she asked me. I knew that what she meant was *fleece*.

'No, not here, we haven't,' I answered, and she looked at me pensively: 'It's strange,' said she, 'that you haven't. That in the villages with plashes there is never white wool.'

White wool? Fleece? 'Though your sins be scarlet they shall be white as wool.' Conscience? Guilt and grief for a wrong-doing? I did not know of any such feeling of guilt: but modern interpreters would say that it would be unconscious if I had. I *do* know why I hate, hate many of the forms of Christianity and other religions however. It is because of the sacrifice at the centre of them—the sacrificial blood.

When we were children our mother gave us raw beef juice. I can remember seeing her scraping the red meat on a board. I loathed it. It made me vibrate with the recoil. Because of that a certain hymn, 'There is a Fountain filled with Blood,' made me feel sick with horror as did the phrase, 'washed in the blood of the lamb.' I believed in life and life if possible free of pain. That is why I wrote just now:

Happiness is divine.

But it was to be experienced by me that one can have too much health. And sanity. And static balance. Health, for all the Greek mistake of it, is not divine, nor even half divine. Ill-health sometimes seems to melt or partly to melt the hardness of the mind.

Another thing which was significant was my turning away from possessions. I was hardly middle aged (39) and very strong and young-looking; and yet there seemed in some mysterious way to be no future. In a dream it might exist but not in truth. There was an end coming, and I mistook that end for death. I wanted no more equipment for life; no more amusements, no more pleasure than the delights of day and night, no more friends. I felt old, and thought with longing of Thoreau's bare cabin, and his bare strength to maintain it so.

It is as difficult and as particular a work to build a view of the universe that one can BE as to build a child's flesh. Day by day the small doses of strength must be given, the vitamins fed to the religion or philosophy which is to grow. Sometimes a sudden ecstasy will seem to confirm the truth. Sometimes as with a child there is sickness and setback. During this winter and spring and summer, an influence affected me that was neither thoughtful nor physical, but unconsciously sympathetic.

Near my sister's house was an Epileptic Colony which helped to support itself by its own farm, which owned several hundred acres and was inhabited by some four hundred men, women and children. There was a school for the children, playing fields, gardens, pigs and a herd of fine Ayrshires. The men and women were kept apart, but moved about freely in the district in pairs or parties. None might go alone outside the grounds.

It was a pleasant enough place with roads and rights-of-way running through it, and we used them almost daily on our roamings. Many and many a time I have pushed my little nephew that way in his pram. When they had attacks the inhabitants often fell down both inside and outside the colony. By some strange chance I never saw even one. It was a well-equipped and well-known epileptic settlement which took in the hopeless cases as well as those who might be 'cured'—or, in truer words, grow out of it with proper treatment. I could remember it since my childhood, but it seemed, contrary to the rest of the neighbourhood, to have grown since the memory. Perhaps it had. It happened that in her girlhood my mother, who sang and played well, had gone very often to do both at the colony concerts. Yet, like myself, she had never seen an epileptic person suffer a fit: indeed, she used to tell me how they would surround any one who fell. She used to think that this was to spare her the sight: but I know now it was the shyness of suffering which I feel myself and the instinctive loyalty towards one another which people afflicted by the same disease show when it is active—a mysterious mass impulse which might make the timid long to enter such a colony rather than attempt to lead a private life which is no longer private. Just so the religious and the thoughtful among human beings congregate. I did, however, know all the symptoms of epilepsy. I had nursed it in dogs.

One evening in early summer when the hawthorn was in bloom, and all the flowers in the different 'house' gardens looked bright and soft, I was lingering in a path there on my way home when I met a woman a little older than myself. She had a quiet, pale, ordinary face, unmarked by the redness which we used to notice, and unmarred by accidents—a face which belonged to the outer world. It showed no signs of disease nor of mental disturbance, it was only profoundly sad.

She spoke first. She smiled and said it was a lovely evening, and didn't the may smell sweet? And then she added, 'I only came here yesterday. It seems a nice place?' She said it as though she was afraid to trust what she saw, and after she had spoken out of what was, I was sure, her forlornness, and as I was going home, there came to me such a sense of her lost liberty, the shocks, the embarrassment and the fear she had had to bear before she had discovered herself standing there in the evening light, that I could never forget it. I felt as if it had happened to myself. Afterwards, often the look of her face came back to me though I never saw her again, its patience and its lasting pathos. It was like a child's who is trying to like its first boarding school. It is a terrible thing to see an expression of youthful pain on an adult face—an unforgettable thing. It is dreadful to be homesick for health. To those who have been healthy and strong, how hard at first are the conditions of illness—any illness which accompanies, as it were, the body without continuous suffering. It must be far easier, I think, to be born an epileptic than to become one—to have to accustom yourself to losing yourself.

I knew the chances were that with modern treatment she might be 'cured.' But I could not forget her; and I see her now and wonder if she had had to sell her home and furniture, or leave a room she was used to living in, and friends. To lose the world which was, it is true, no longer adapted to her, yet familiar, all because of this stranger in her brain.

It does seem a strange coincidence indeed that I, who was free and went in and out and saw the poor children and the sad, bitter, battered faces of the older inhabitants, and the 'different' ones of the younger, should have been all the time one of them. It explains the movement of my mind towards them, the extraordinary sympathy which was like affinity, and the curiosity (for it *was* curiosity) which could never forget to speculate upon their feelings, though I saw them so often that I should have accepted and forgotten them. It was strange, but in no way prophetic unless the brain knows what it does not tell to the mind, as the body knows what it does not tell to the brain. Because there has never been any epilepsy on either side of my family and no physical-mental illness whatever.

However, she may have become contented, if she were not discharged. There are reserves of freedom, and in all restrictions people find them and live in them. In a Universe where all things nourish one another, surely there can be no absolute loss?

CHAPTER V

Ir I were naming these divisions of my story, I should call this one 'The Disappearance.' For during part of August in the year 1949, all the symptoms (which, of course, I did not recognize as being anything of the kind) disappeared, including the oldest of them all, which I have not yet attempted to describe, but will do so now. I cannot recall when I was without moments of separation from my consciousness—moments when I was quite literally conscious and unconscious at the same time. But as my memory is faulty it may not really have been since young childhood. For instance, of memory in sequence I have none. Remembrance with me is a matter of the emotion I spent. It appears to me that unless I have been emotionally 'blown up' either by ecstasy or grief, I cannot remember anything at all except faces, hands, furniture, places, etc., detached from any particular event or spoken words. I do *feel*, however, that this consciousness superimposed on unconsciousness has been with me a long while. And here, I must be careful, for this is epilepsy itself, though in its minor form; and should any one read this and recognize it in himself, he should go to a doctor at once. I never did. I never thought of it as anything more than a momentary but natural pressure, due possibly to my defective eyes, or wax in the ears or some uninteresting unhygienic trifle of that kind. Through all the small illnesses and consequent interviews with doctors since I was grown up and responsible for myself, I never mentioned it—the one tiny thing that mattered and meant so much future trouble. How can it be described? It came often after I had been stooping—scrubbing the cottage floors perhaps, or planting seeds in our gardens, which was what made me connect it with momentary pressure.

It caused no pain, it lasted a few seconds, I saw and heard and moved while it happened. I have often crossed a room, and, while not losing sight or bearings, not known *how* I crossed it. The sequence of consciousness was so little broken by it, that after it had happened it seemed not an atom of time or myself had been missing, and I only knew it had happened again by the numb sensation in the centre of the brain which followed it. I do not get it now that the major attacks have superseded it; and that makes it still more difficult to be accurate in recollection. I do, however, remember laughing to my husband about my 'little wheel,' going off again. It seemed like a tiny wheel—the wheel say, of a watch, whirring at blurring speed, quite soundlessly, in my head while I went on with whatever I was doing, guided by *the consciousness left over* rather than the consciousness of the moment.

The wheel would then cease, and there was a loud silence such as follows a blow on a drum, also in my head. A clanging ache followed that. The whole thing took about as long as for a normal person to walk five paces, say.

These spells became more frequent and longer and *darker* during the year 1948 than at any other time in my life. I was then aware of there being at the heart of a second, oblivion of mind and cessation of sight. During the spring and summer of 1949, which I am describing, I had only two of them, both of which strangely enough I remember, and both of which still more strangely occurred on the same spot.

When they have happened to me while crossing a room I have, if I may so illustrate it, left myself on one side and come to myself on the other, while feeling an atom of time divided the two selves, as the room might divide the figures of myself, supposing any one could create two figures of me. And this is important to the story, because 'the two figures' idea became so strong later and so haunting just before each major fit that I had later, that I was afraid of there being, or there being danger of being, a real split in me. It took me a whole year of suffering and possibly a dozen major fits, to disentangle myself from the terror of mental disorder, and to discover by hard meditation the true state I was in during that dreaded moment of double bodiedness. Has not every one of us a mental image of himself which he watches ceaselessly, which he must watch, and which must not, for his health's and sanity's sake, deviate from the self seen by everybody else? I believe it could be so: that this mental image and exact reproduction may have been accepted and understood from very ancient days—that it may in fact have been the birth of the forever unconfirmed, forever believed in idea of a soul. And that most certainly the object of a great deal of evil magic and witchcraft was aimed at this mental image—at its distortion and division from the physical one, causing insanity or death. Such an idea would seem to be connected with many religions and superstitions and customs particularly with those appertaining to the human shadow. The shadow was the nearest embodiment or realization of the mental image by which is accompanied our every action while sane and conscious, that these first people could think of. Thus it became a thing to which harm could be done, or which could cause harm.

I write of this here, sure only of its lack of value to

anybody but myself among the living. Sure only of my lack of knowledge. But sure also that knowledge could give no answer but an opinion.

Who has benefited more by knowledge than I, who have been saved by it from torture? Who could revere and admire learning and certainty and all intellectual accomplishment more passionately than I, who have no capacity for them? The love of learning is like the love of beauty—we must adore it, and not having it, adore and end with adoration. Yet for all that I ask myself, and would like to ask others—*What is it to know?* Does it bring certainty? Does it bring peace? Satisfaction? In the end does it bring knowledge? Or is it like geography, the vaster the continent, the greater the boundaries, the less known the wild coasts? To live in ignorance—can it be that to live in ignorance is to live on an island, tiny perhaps, but permitting the same vision of the same profound inescapable sky?

But my story . . . these very minute attacks which I have tried to describe were the first sign of a difference, nevertheless, between my conscious body and what I have called its mental image, its twin in action. And the last two of them took place on the same spot. There was a most beautiful beech-wood about a mile from our home when we were children at St. Ides. I was now living with my sister in the house next door to that old home; and one afternoon soon after I first went there, in January or February of 1949, I set off to look at it. The Cathedral, we had called it. I was sure of my direction, yet I could not find it. There was the little river, now dry, the willows and the slope of fields beyond. And there inexplicably was a farmhouse, a very old farmhouse where none had been.

Of course the wood had been cut down and the farm revealed. But it took me some roaming and searching to be certain of this. At last I stood on the winter grass where the last night's frost was still blue in the shadow of the blackberry bushes, looking on the ruins of the Cathedral. They *were* ruins. Many a bombed and fire-gutted church that the green weeds and nettles and briars are smoothing and hiding, looks like the hacked and torn wood looked then, where the 'haughty' beeches had stood over their shoals of clean brown leaves when I was a child of ten.

I looked: with the sense of loss came a memory of running away from home and hiding under those trees for a whole day when I was supposed to go back to boarding school. I had known very nearly nothing at ten—I could hardly read at nine—relatively my knowledge in childhood approximates to my knowledge in adult age—I lived in my instincts and those emotions which were to be my only true memories. And the time came back to me—the misery, the desolation, the lack of courage which could only take me so far and then must return me as surely as a policeman to the home I feared. Feared only because of its loss. When those who have been our protectors turn of necessity into a force which is not with us in the sense that children understand it, oh who can believe the grief to a child? Only the person who has grown out of that child and remembers it.

I looked, however, very quietly; and at that moment the busy dizziness began—the watch wheel went round and round at the base of my brain, and as I turned and walked quite steadily away, I had the sensation of something left behind by the bramble bushes. I think that that time I staggered as the silence came and the two 'images' fused. Anyway I was cold and grieved and hurried home. The next time the same thing happened as I peered into what had once been the Cathedral, it was summer; and if—which seems hardly possible—the resurrection of that dreary pain felt by a child, could have helped to cause the spasm of the brain, certainly the possibility was ruled out on the second occasion. For I had often been there since and had quite stopped remembering *as a feeling* what had happened to me there. I simply knew it as one knows the facts of anybody else's life: it was no longer as vivid as the place to me.

The second time everything was just as it had been the first, as it had been countless times before and I thought nothing about it, as usual. The coincidence was the second of two, where my illness was concerned, and later I shall have to describe the first.

That summer of 1949 a wonderful pleasure happened to me which helped me immensely in every way. This was my being awarded a literary holiday—a sum of money anonymously given to not well-known authors, usually younger than myself, was declared to be mine for that year. There were no conditions except that the money was to be spent out of England and that the donator was to remain unknown to the receiver. The news of this came on Good Friday: I was stunned with delight for mine has not been financially a rewarding career and the thought of a holiday abroad was something which made me absolutely shake with joy. It was years since I had left England . . . the day the letter came we went by car to the lovely flat country around the small Thames: and everything I saw, even the running water and the big meadow full of fritillary buds seemed stopped in full flow and growth like myself at a moment of perfection. Many people have been called ungrateful in this life, not because they are, but because they have had few causes for gratitude.

I was at once so grateful, so mystified and so astonished that it was as if I had known this holiday was to be fitted in, as it were, at the end, or almost the end of 'normal' health.

And it was as perfect as the first moment. We went to Ireland, my husband and myself. A journal which I kept was not for ourselves, but for my Benefactor and I later sent it through the secret channels which reached this extraordinarily alive and humane heart. The unknown personality who had given me such pleasure went with me wherever I went, to the sea, to the hills, to the mystic ruins of tall towers, to the old libraries and the beauties of Dublin's most beautiful city. So that I have no record of our journeyings, which in any case would be out of place here. All that matters to this narrative is the disappearance, during the time we were away, of every sign of any ailment. The headaches, the sloping giddiness, the dizzy attacks, the depressions which paid for the exaltations of being, all disappeared. Mentally I was as clear as the country unspoiled by traffic, as calm as the long, long roads where sheep and cattle and donkeys took the place of ghastly speed and hideous shapes. And again it was pictures of natural things I took back in my mind—the dark colour and the feeling of arbutus leaves touched on the West Coast, the Atlantic waves weaving seaweed with waxy foam, the heather on top of a high hill swung by bees like a breeze, for these were my cures. And the brain, knowing before it tells of its malady, seeks for the cure. And mine, as it always had, went its country way, a herbalist of a brain, a gatherer of simples.

CHAPTER VI

In his *Poet's Journal*, that pathetic description of a poverty much greater and more self-denying than my own, George Crabbe writes—'the Muse would never visit till the purse was recruited, for, say men what they will, she does not love empty pockets nor poor living.'

And that, poor mortgaged Crabbe, is true. If the Muse be saleable, she can manage on her own; but if she be a creature of midnight failures, who yet cannot be cut off, like a telephone or a wireless that is out of order, and *will* persist in communicating sound whatever one wishes, she will nevertheless go on demanding the privileges of income however small—i.e. food, an empty room, time to meditate and to premeditate. Inspiration is a torment then. And what is this Inspiration which so many doubt, and so many falsify and distort, calling it a light in itself, an easy ascent, as by another will than one's own. *Inspiration is longing.* One can be inspired to learn, as one can be inspired to translate what is already planned and formed in the mind. Inspiration is a yearning so intense to make sensible in visible or oral form what has already been foreseen and heard within the brain that it must be attempted at all costs, including the cost of health. And it simply does not reckon with repayment. It is, however, almost beyond human power to go on without repayment, if one is without income. The telephone, which is the Muse (and the Muse is not inspiration but its controlling power), if one may continue with the analogy, continues to ring incessantly,

45

one answers, as one is bound to do, but the charges are reversed.

How far my financial failures as a writer contributed to the worry of living and bore perhaps indirectly, but too heavily, on a thin spot in my mentality: how much worry can contribute towards a physical explosion, I am not in a position to answer. But I should think in my own case not a lot. I think that I myself built up the disease within me, but that its climax was inevitable because I am myself. It did not arrive yet: there were other preliminaries to the voyage, as well as all the accustomed ones to be gone through. As soon as I arrived in England—which seemed very suffocating and crowded—the headaches, the dizzy spells and the true symptoms of epilepsy in minor form, began again together with the hurried, intangible excitement which never allowed me to spend myself long on anything except writing. That, as usual, I did at night, but there were no pines now to hear in the shadow of the wind, but the clocks of a city in hourly converse, and the Cathedral chimes. I was living in Gloucester with my sister-in-law and my husband had begun his two years at a teaching college.

I look back on that period as one of comparative peace, ease and freedom. As the winter came on I decided that as there was no longer any sale at all for my short prose pieces and I was not yet ripe enough to attempt my final novel—never written—or the book on Emily Brontë on whom I had written an essay which would bear expansion, or rather inclusion, in a larger form, what I needed to keep my mental powers warm, was some good hard intellectual effort. I chose the sonnet, and to read the psalms. Rhythmically they did not agree at all; but my brain longed to attack this strict form of poetry. I felt sure that, sufficiently digested, it could clothe any thought, could fall about it as softly, naturally and inevitably as foliage about a willow tree. I didn't write one good sonnet; yet by ceaseless and very late effort—it was nearly always three before I went to bed to read a psalm—the shape and the stresses and the stern iambic pentameters *did* become natural, and I could think in them without being cut off by a limb: my later efforts flowed—but they were very bad. And my diaries which have always been my temptations flowed too in streams of impressions. I earned nothing, and not my own approval for I became less and less companionable to myself except when in the third presence of Nature, or, as I began to believe, God. I loved my own company but I did not admire it, whereas I loved, admired, adored and was absorbed by the countryside I could reach on those short, cold, dark afternoons. I remember meeting a hare—and watching immense fugues of starlings over the flats.

The hurry, which was like a heart beating in my head, grew so bad that I wondered nobody noticed it. Here is a significant short note in one diary—

November 23rd. 'I'm feeling very low in health. Haven't any *continuation*. Everything is disconnected from me and from everything else. Existence is just an ache in the head.'

And another undated bit:

'She (I) comes panting through the alleys, her breath at her mouth, crying "my heart has vanished." Truly it is better to DIE than to vanish into Life.'

There is mention too of the loss of 'divine hush.' And after that, 'In thy Presence is Fulness of Joy.' And then I wrote a little afterwards:

'I love the dogs. Their feet are my companions and the pleasure they get out of wayside things amuses me and makes me forget my own *lack of vitality*.'

47

Lack of vitality! I who a few years ago had hoed beet with the men, kept house in a cottage, gardened and written *Autobiography*. Truly it was coming nearer, this disease, this darkness which is so hard to read.

My spaniel was always with me. My thoughts of Death had returned to be with me too, and one night a dream combined them. I dreamed that my Rosie (the spaniel) reached up to the mantelpiece and took down first a skull, and then a tiny figure or ornament. I examined this figure in the dream; and it was Death with his scythe and his grin, all minute, all detailed and finished, in yellow skeleton bone.

My sister-in-law found us a cottage in the country and I longed for it, but one day when no one was in the room I looked in the mirror and saw that my face was too old to begin again. And whenever I met our landlord-to-be I used to ask him half in dread, half in yearning how long it would be before it was ready.

The dream just described was the beginning of a spell of nightmares. It wasn't pleasant to wake from a sort of D.T.'s of things partly seen, in a room alone at the top of the old house: but what made it worse was that it was the third attack or series of nightmares in my life. And the last one I could not avoid remembering, a doctor had taken very seriously indeed. I was about seventeen when they happened: I had no wish to tell him or anybody about them but I was compelled to at last in defence of what was left of my courage. I thought he would laugh too, and I should have to look a fool. But having made me describe one of them we went through a dialogue which was like this:

THE DOCTOR. Have you ever had any dreams like this before?

MYSELF. Yes.

THE DOCTOR. When?

MYSELF. When I was about three years old.

THE DOCTOR. Do you remember them clearly?

MYSELF. Yes, terribly.

THE DOCTOR. Do you remember anything else when you were that age?

MYSELF. No, I don't think so. The doctor we had then told my mother to move me into her room, but I don't remember that.

THE DOCTOR. How do you know that that was what he said?

MYSELF. Because my mother told me. Afterwards.

THE DOCTOR. Were those dreams exactly like these?

MYSELF. No, they weren't. They were worse.

THE DOCTOR. You can probably bear them better now. What were they?

MYSELF. They were fire—all fire. And people running, all on fire with fire behind them. I can remember what they looked like. They were nuns. I shall never forget them.

THE DOCTOR. You could never have seen anything really at all like them?

MYSELF. I don't see how I could have. They were *dying*. I have never seen any nuns on fire, dying and I don't see how a child could imagine them either, do you?

THE DOCTOR. No, I don't. Did you see anything else besides these figures?

MYSELF. I saw my great-aunt step out of a train and she was all on fire too. I must have been in a ghastly disaster in another life, I think.

THE DOCTOR. (*Impatiently*). Well, I can't help you to understand that or interpret your horrors for you, but I'm giving you a sleeping draught, and if you ever have any more of those dreams you are to come straight to me. Do you understand? At once. They aren't *right*. A girl of your age shouldn't have them.

I have given this description of my earliest dream-horrors in this form because it is the shortest. What the doctor meant, or what he was thinking, I did not ask, nor did he tell me. It was not these forms of terrible entreaty in their capes of flame I saw in later life: and certainly my mind was better prepared to endure what it *did* see. If a child is unable to separate its identity or personality from the things it sees, it is still less able to observe itself separately from its dreams. But I was now approaching middle age and used to dreaming dreadful and beautiful things. And so the effect was less. Also I did take a kind of pride in these visions; for if I have any theory about dreaming it is certainly not the sex-psychological one developed by most of the great searchers of the unconscious mind: but that to dream at all shows imagination, and to dream as furiously as I could shows an extremely powerful creative faculty. And this has always pleased me. If I wished to choose a companion, of my own free will, to talk to (which I don't), I should begin the search by asking the applicants: 'Do you dream?' People who do not are invariably dull.

It is not possible for me to theorize as to whether the nun dreams with the raging fire, or the death dreams, had any connection with epilepsy or brain trouble of any sort: but there was one repeated dream which I think began during the autumn and winter of 1949-50, which seems most emphatically to have done so. It might have started before. It was not, I am sure, a dream, but a sensation in sleep—in short, a fit during sleep, not so slight as my dizzy double consciousness which came when I stooped and not so severe as a major epileptic fit. I could not have gone quite out, or there would have been no mind to record the memory, no bodily sensation to experience it. I did and I do remember what I then thought was this particularly queer, unpleasant dream every time I had it. And I do not care to think how often that was. I seemed to remember a time in the night when my muscles had gone rigid, my teeth locked, and I was shaken by a kind of ghastly iron palsy. My arms seemed to lift, my head to jerk and my face to be covered with a grimace. Most strange of all I always related this experience not to myself but to my sister who has assuredly never had a fit in her life, and whom it is not possible I could ever have seen as I have a mental picture of her, distorted, in that attitude of tense agony which it is so hard for many people to believe is unconscious and painless.

Never could I have seen my sister like this: and yet the sight haunts me. Indeed, I have never seen a complete epileptic fit in my life except in dogs: when I questioned my husband about my attitudes and gestures during one, they did not at all resemble this extraordinary and horrible vision. So that it would appear that my mind is not only obstinately determined to see my sister as myself, but to see her incorrectly. This seems really mysterious and inexplicable to me.

If it takes imagination to make a dream in the same way that it does to make a story or a scene in a story, the pleasure is very much modified by the imagination being the cause of the reaction to the dream—i.e. in the case of the reader who has imagination to be able to imagine the scene of the story, it is, of course, unmitigatedly good, but in the case of the dreamer who is both the creator and the reactor to the vision, the effect is certainly the more horrifying, as the power to react to the scene is as strong as the power to erect the dream. I did not suffer as I had as a screaming, maddened child of three, but I did suffer. I had also extremely beautiful dreams when the power of life and beauty itself seemed extended, and my powers of perception with them. Thus my nights, as in a sense my days, followed in a measure the pattern of the manic-depressive's and those of people who have put themselves in experiment under nitrous oxide.

CHAPTER VII

I CONSIDER that with this 'dream' of rigid shaking my state as a person subject to major epileptic fits really began. I think so now: I did not then. I did not consider myself in any way abnormal or different from any one else. How should I? My periods of unhappiness seemed less profound and more controllable than many of the people I knew who are sound to-day. I was often unhappy, over excited, restless and disappointed that I could not drive myself out of myself to write my novel. (That seems to me a sin to this day that I did not, for what was all the rest?) But mentally I was full of life, of speculation and observation. Thus for half an hour at a time I would watch flights of starlings above the roofs: the figures of the great and the godlike were with me though Apollo had retreated into that past summer with the brook and the honeysuckle; I thought daily of Bach and that great Austrian liutaro, Jacob Stainer, whose frightful life and death is so abominable a slur upon human perceptiveness. To this grand man whose pauper's hands, scarred by chains, had fashioned the rare and beautiful violins now sought throughout the world, I wrote one of my sonnets—the only one at that time which stood on its own, unpropped as it seemed by my words. Campion was my poet, with his 'silent music'; Campion's was the poem whose phrase

> Sing thou smoothly with thy beauty's
> silent music

led me into meditating on the absolutely different nature of music and poetry, all of which kept my mind a whole mind still, though the voyage had begun, and the ship was soon to breathe up and down in the rhythm of the oceans and the seamen gaze round on only loneliness and sky.

It is said that epileptic people have violent tempers—'an epileptic rage' seems a stale phrase to me. Whether this is so or not I cannot say, but many abstract questions at this time seemed to anger me, such as this one of music and poetry. I would become very cross, as well as bewildered and contrary every time some one alluded to this (for me) non-existent relationship between mankind's two greatest expressions. It was perhaps connected with the fact that I have never heard great poetry spoken or acted but have always read it to myself: also I tried to teach myself the violin and went far enough with that and the keyboard, bad as I was at both, to discover for myself the unsatisfactoriness of listening to music instead of making it. With one you are inside the music, with the other you are an outsider only, a mere oral spectator if such words are possible. One is a vocation, the other a pleasure. Even further apart and more separate are music and poetry, one being a solution of sound, the other its meaning:

> I never heard the organ
> I never heard the sea
> I never heard even a bird,
> in any poetry.
>
> Great rolling Milton is as dumb
> As any desert sand,
> And Shelley wrote like those quiet folk
> who speak upon the hand.

But if this glorious music lack
its zenith of being heard,
the more it must resemble the
still genius of God.

The verses are partly the effect of my solitary reading. But the point is an old one with me; and I shall never understand the confusion, or fusing of the two arts. No really fine poem ever gained anything by being set to even the loveliest music: no really divine vocal music needs anything more than syllables. That the two arts can inspire each other none but an idiot would deny; but that is not the same thing.

I used to meditate upon such things when indoors; as I meditated upon the figure of Jacob Stainer whose image dominated that winter of 1949-50 for me. Was I trying to make up to him for some of that agony of his life, in my small way? When Humanity has committed a great injustice to a great man, or against a fine art, there will always be people whose pity and fury will seemingly attempt to reverse the past. People who have no money and no influence: for the world of man in its *commercial* way has long confessed one of its most brutal refusals to protect and prolong the life of a rare genius.

I seem diffuse. Nor is it possible for me to doubt that I am. But such a diffusion of mental activity is probably incidental to the illness which was now rapidly approaching. And if I unintentionally reveal more than I know I am revealing, it is so much the more valuable to the reader who understands.

Many of the notes written that winter are burned, for there were account books, exercise books and scribbling blocks crowded with poems and writing, as my brain was crowded with impressions. These note-books were my vent, but they exhausted me and wasted my night hours, and made impossible any objective writing whatever. The ceaseless interestingness of natural life continued for me, but now it excited rather than soothed me. Even the quietest of sights on my walks outside and around the town, even the most well known and well trodden of them stimulated my already over-active mental existence. Nothing seemed too ordinary: the commonplace grass of the towpath would hold my attention like a curiosity: the jackdaws flapping round the cathedral tower, the sight of a solitary wild duck on the marshy meres among the rushes became pageants to be caught in words—and words— and more words. I think I came to realize this because my writing had always been so sparing of itself that I had had to search for it, whereas now it flooded everything. The room was full of papers—a turmoil of them covered chairs and chests and floor. To revert from my conscious mental activity to my unconscious—the bad dreams lasted only a short while. The phase may have been as long as a week or a little longer. Their effect was small —it was only to make me grip the more hard to any- thing of the earth within reach. The opposite rarer dreams I had perhaps twice or thrice during the whole winter.

And here, though one must be careful, there is little chance of accuracy. Once more I must revert to John Custance's book, for it is the only one on abnormality *by* an abnormal person I have read. It is very noticeable in *Wisdom, Madness and Folly*, how easily its author described his evil or depressive phases compared with his rarer ecstatic or exalted ones. A lunatic might perhaps be described as living asleep, as acting in a dream, bad or good? A dreamer, even a normal dreamer can always describe the details of an evil dream much more easily than a beautiful one. Beauty so occupies and so transfuses the spirit that it seems, to an observant entity, to vanish into joy. Of these enormous and ecstatic dreams of mine I can remember almost nothing, and what I do recollect of sensation will not go into words. I must give an idea of them simply by negatives—i.e. they were not of people, they were never of persons, but always of place—a place. They contained no sex, and provoked no sensations of sex. Finally that I am aware that the reverse of them would not be evil, but *unhappiness*. I was to learn the reverse, as will be seen. Thus they were not the complement of my nightmares, or the opposite of my horrors. Rather they were in opposition to all things cruel, all things grievous, all things discordant. That they were, however they arrived, the most perfect expression of joy, peace and gaiety, anything in this life has ever brought me. There was colour in them, space, and a kind of radiant liberty such as Thoreau describes in *Waldon* when he was watching the solitary flight of a young hawk. And it is only while seeing by chance, some *secret freedom* in animal, bird, insect or flower, or tree, while unobserved—I could almost say unexisting—myself, I have ever been faintly reminded of something definite in those dreams which is absent in all the rest of life. The faint reminder is enough to teach me how unrestrainedly one who strove for such a vision of unity and power and peace would pursue it, gladly leaving life and health and sanity to attain it. The pursuit of it is not normal, nor healthy, nor perhaps good. At least I doubt it. But it is inevitable. This way, I am sure, went Emily Brontë. This way, but for a more sanguine love of Jesus Christ, would have been the path of George Herbert who at twenty-two wrote in a strange mystical poem, this verse inferior to none of his loveliest later ones.

> Now I am here, what thou wilt do with me
> None of my books will show;
> I read and sigh, and wish I were a tree;
> for then sure I should grow
> to fruit or shade; at least some bird would trust
> her household to me, and I should be just.

'Just' I take to mean 'at peace' and a remarkably good word for that state it is.

There are three simple words which indicate, if they cannot describe, the beatitude of such vision. They are: 'Love, joy, peace.' And in that order they are used by Mrs. Beecher Stowe to describe what was seen by her child heroine on her death-bed. These days they may be laughed at, or that particular scene be mocked: but the fact is that it was as prescient on the part of Mrs. Beecher Stowe when she wrote them, as the description in *Great Expectations* of Pip in the contracted hideousness of delirium, when he imagined himself a brick in a wall. Both are perfectly accurate, or as accurate as words can be seeing that words are all either remembrance or prophecy.

If we are to live and to continue to be mentally healthy individuals, religion must interpose itself between us and such joy. Habitual religion, such as Herbert's. God must intervene between us and nature. God *is* Nature, to those who can discover Him (or as I would rather write IT) nowhere else. He is everything we love or enjoy that does not distort ourselves. Or so I believe. For the attainments of other forms of life are beyond us, weighted as we are by intellect. Is this the meaning of the world-wide symbol of the birth of man in a garden—that we must worship on

our knees where once we worshipped on wings? That
animals and trees and plants, but not man, exist in a state
of beatitude?

Sonnet I

They never told me why my God was man,
they told me sacrificial stories of a rite,
dividing him in tributaries of father, son and light
for my soul's sake—of which blood was the plan.

They did not tell me, nothing yet outran
the one embracing circle of delight
and destiny and love man is for man
and all he learns and guesses of a greater might.

That God was flesh and had a Son
because we must learn his *our* way of love
they never said: God would be God—begun
for each of us afresh, which is both's proof
that he was flesh, and we shall soon be soul,
and he with us and we with him are one.

Sonnet II

Oh all of space, oh purest all indeed!
oh root whose petals are in Paradise,
oh love who dost not seek our eyes,
oh love! whose only gift to us is need,
whose tenderness is we should fall and bleed,
whose silence never answers our replies,
oh loveliness, of which each beauty cries
it is a copy! Track it to its seed—

Oh God whose only yearning is our own,
an echo of ourselves when we are still,
why dost thou in our searching, seem to call us home

through anything we love, come, come oh come
leaving thy reasons, letting fall thy will,
bringing thine all, leaving behind thy some?

Sonnet III

Why do we worship? Why adoring
name God as Goodness which is Grief?
Seek for a reason: thou shalt find it brief
a single surety about thee soaring.
God is Credible: where thy love is poring
be it on man or nature there is his belief.
Dost thou love flesh? dost watch a leaf?
thy God was flesh: in grass God, God is storing.

Dost thou love healing? God is healing.
Science or Inspiration? into these
himself he streams, and in the tempests reeling
in transports underneath the summer trees
that men call madness; and in dumb idiocies.
And where his being is denied he will be feeling,
oh unavoidable, in Denial too revealing!

CHAPTER VIII

ONE day in March 1950, the cottage was ready for occupation and I left my sister-in-law's in Gloucester to begin to
live there. My husband, who was on his first year's teaching
course at St. Paul's College, Cheltenham, was to come home
at the week-ends only. For the village was six miles from
Cheltenham and was at the top of a very long and exhaust-
ing hill—a steep three-quarters of a mile.

The village stood at nearly a thousand feet high and was
really small, without shop or pub. There was one charming
woman who sold salt, flour and sweets from a cupboard
off her back kitchen; and a post office in a garden full of
snowdrops both of which were a delight to visit. All food
and other supplies were delivered from the towns. Milk
was fetched from the one farm at half past four every
afternoon. The water was recently acquired: the lighting
was by paraffin lamps, the countryside was bare and
beautiful and grew many quite rare wild flowers. In autumn
the woods were flooded with the autumn crocus, and in
spring there flourished in them the wild hellebore, the
Herb Paris, wild garlic; water heliotrope soaked up at
least one marshy meadow. Everywhere one walked, the
rarer orchis were a possibility; and all summer the wild
geranium coloured the roadsides and tracks with its transparent purple and vermilion spurs.

The church was old and famous. Outside it looked
fairly large but there was a mere kernel of shadowed space
inside with coloured pieces of light thrown over a tiny
altar by a very small east window like a patchwork cushion-

cover. The whole renowned building was wreathed inside and out by ornaments of carved animals, snakes, birds and people. There were two heads that looked something like crocodiles and we used to wonder where those early artists could have seen them.

We had neither of us any business with the church: but it was so compelling that whenever one was near it, it called one to it. In the graveyard were many exceedingly fine tombs, carved as originally as the church itself. One had figures of two priest-like forms in windy robes with strange hats like harebells. They held books, but did not look Christian. The same restless wind that was always blowing at that height seemed tossing their skirts, so that the figures were extraordinarily alive, as if they were living in the same present atmosphere as the spectator. They made their impression on me and I had to draw them before I could get them out of my mind. The trees were mostly beech or ash and at that height there was little tree fruit, but only bushes and strawberries. I did not expect when I went to live there half the beauty that came magnificently forward with the spring: the climate was late, a month behind the valleys; but when the spring came at last and the leaves, they did not as they do in luxurious places, take away the shapes of things, but simply changed the colours of those pure contours to a shining green. I was only to live there one year, but never to gain so much of the intangibleness of a place as I did there. Nature is the mother, and the inclination to live and to admire must begin with the mother. But the discovery of God is the child finding that it can get its food elsewhere than from the mother. It is a weaning from, but not away from, the mother. I think such nature mystics as Richard Jefferies are never weaned. Many, however, do not achieve even birth from the mother; and especially these days, do not live because their consciousness of life is stillborn. I was miles from the country where I had been reared and which I had violently and exclusively loved; but to those who are bound to the leaf, it does not matter where the leaf is, indeed the more precious, the more difficult its presence, it seems. That year in E—— I used to walk in the beech-woods with my dog and track the streams through the huge, hilly fields, whatever else distracted me. I used to put out my hands and stroke the grass, or the leaves by my side, and I thought that in the touch I had discovered the presence and hermitage of God. I thought this quite calmly and humbly, not in wild states of joy or fear.

Very strangely, during this year, 1950, Derek Savage brought out a critique of modern writers: one of whom he chose was myself, and in his essay on my novels, concluding with an examination of the essays which took the book-form of *Autobiography*, he mentioned the inner sadness, hollowness and final despair of the 'nature-cult.' *Autobiography* he found spiritually wanting. He detected within it the death wish, which I call not the death wish but the death obsession, and which I have attempted to describe and have myself associated with my epilepsy. The point was not that, however, though I thought it brilliant of him to discover it, but the spiritual incomplete-ness. I wrote to this most just and fair critic, and told him that, as I was not dead, neither was *Autobiography* spiritually speaking finished, and that I hoped yet to develop. At E—— I felt that I was growing both before and after the major attacks began; and I feel now that this story of my brain is in fact the second part of *Autobiography* and belongs to it. I take back nothing of the first, my thought now, however reverently I may acknowledge God, is not

Christian, and mine will never be the Christian consciousness because of my hatred of blood and sacrifice. And this hopefulness that there is God and that God made us and everything is what I meant by the passage quoted by Derek Savage: 'I am not lonely. I should only be lonely if I happened alone, if I existed alone, if I had to make myself breathe. If I had created myself and must decide for myself when to die, then I should be lonely . . .'

That passage seems clearly to me to describe a belief in a Creator, if no more; and at this date when we had begun our life at E—— I could still admit it as my truth while every day my being drew closer to this Creator, to God's physical being, and also unknown to me, to his darkness. The end of *Autobiography*, with its resignation to death, was not an end but my prophecy of what was to become of me and what was to grow more intelligible to me.

It seems to me that an implicit faith in a creator is everywhere indicated in everything I have written. It is unconscious perhaps, as unconscious and more so than the 'death wish' which Derek Savage associated with a desire for rest. This longing for rest in my brain is now explained: it is, if it is a death longing, the innocent one of the physically exhausted. And taking it from its purely functional religious viewpoint, I ask, have not all ardent Christians desired death? Did not Blake, did not Goethe? The small ones among us are not different from the great; we are only less expressive and less lovely. Our impulses are exactly the same.

Not that I fear the words which are taken up as wars and used against us. I fear them no more than Thoreau feared poverty. The word 'Escapist,' for instance, and the word 'Egotist.' To escape the daily round of thought and conviction, to see not the world in ourselves, but ourselves in the world, are not these achievements for freedom? Nobody who has gained even the smallest amount of control over language fears its application to himself. Words are tools to the writer. If one hurl a hammer at my head, am I a blow?

People who suffer from epilepsy *are* egoists. They must try to be themselves and cling to themselves more than normal people, for they are likely any moment to become something else. But before I go on to my story I should like to say something about the word egotist. The dictionary defines the word as one who makes too much use of the pronoun 'I': nothing could be more helpful to me here in this paragraph than that. I am aware that the incessant 'I' exists in this MS. almost as frequently as if I were a mad-woman. It could be cut out or cut down by half at least, but only by writing roundabout sentences and by using the forced and unconvincing 'one.' Therefore I have not attempted it though it is as unpleasant to write as to read.

Is there not something that is not ugly, not selfish, not greedy in being an egoist? The ego, being the self, the consciousness, is also the judge of all moral conduct, and the more alive and prevalent the ego, the more actively the judge will preside. How shall I do unto my neighbour as I would he should do unto me, if I know not what I would he should do? I cannot begin. With my knowledge, my expertness in myself begins my understanding of others' needs. It is my only guide. The one who remembers his own childhood will never go wrong with children: he who remembers himself, when others need him, will not fail them. The Self is the pattern. The judge. The criterion. When the Self is innocent of wrong, wrong has not been. I had a small example of this the other day. Having got on a bus, I discovered I thought that I had left all my money at home. As I went to get off, I told the conductor. He said, 'Stay on, if you can manage without the money in the town. Don't get off. Help one another.'

I stayed on, and only when walking up a street found my purse in a pocket. Then I began to ask myself *why* I had wronged no one? The conductor didn't know and would never know that I could have paid my fare. So he could not exonerate me. Who did? My Self out of everybody on earth, singled me out and judged me not guilty of a petty fraud that mattered not at all. If the Self can do this and has not lost its sense of justice, no one need dread being an Egoist. Innocence may radiate from the Ego as powerfully as guilt. Abstemiousness, freedom, poverty, heroism, faith are all egoistic qualities. The martyrs were certainly Egoists for they believed that they mattered to God. This is supreme Egoism. And the opposite are the narrow, the cruel, the driven spirits, who have believed the reverse, whose lives were examples of men whose faith was that God was *their* concern, and *they* must stir Him into action who said in Isaiah: My Thoughts are not your thoughts and my ways are not your ways.

What is wrong with *Autobiography* is the strain, the intensity, the continuous effort to put into language what was in reality a deeply relaxing experience. There have never been times so social, so incessantly interchanging, times with so many interviews with mankind as our times. Too much response is demanded, too much stimulation indulged in. My meditations as I walked and watched were the reverse of all this. At least they were until my brain became over excitable. The lapsing into quietude, which I failed to convey in *Autobiography* because it was words, was what saved me for so long.

As Thoreau refused to have a doormat because it would draw other domestic elaborations after it, we kept out of the range of the wireless. I hate machinery and fear electricity. Relaxing when the strange harried excitement of my mind would let me into the sight of fields, trees and animals, I was happy. We tore up the matted garden and planted it with flowers and vegetables. I found the spring, for we had no fresh water, and until my neighbours up the road gave me permission, carried the buckets full of clear, liquid ice, a quarter of a mile and up a steep grass bank. We used oil lamps. It was a hard, rough, tiring life, but to us it was life, and not served up stale on a tepid plate like a town meal.

There was not a great deal of time for wandering except on errands such as carrying home bean sticks. (I brought home two dozen poles, three or four at a time, more than a mile uphill.) Weariness brings misery, and I was most miserable sometimes. My joy, my hope, my belief was out of breath: the gardening and the cleaning seemed to take all the time, and only late at night when tired and worn out was I free to write. I remember the envy I felt towards the Brontë sisters, and the life which allowed them some one to cook for them, and freedom to walk and to write. It was as passionate as if they were living women and my neighbours. People thought them tragic, spoke and wrote of their unhappy lives when they had all that *I* wanted of this world. How I hated them! Bitterness and envy joined me and I suffered from a sense of being wronged and deprived, or as they would say now, frustrated. Still I went on at night by lamplight with my despairing notes that could never achieve the beauty of that place, with my sonnets and my unwanted poems. The form I had chosen for the sonnets was the one I prefer, the Italian, the one

Milton and Wordsworth made wonderful for ever.[1] That is the most beautiful, I believe, though in my opinion William Drummond, who used the Shakespearian form, is the greatest sonneteer in the English language. But even in him, and in Shakespeare, I never liked the concluding couplet: also the opening eight lines lack the lovely return on one another that the Italian rhyme scheme causes—a slow swirl, a calm backward sweep such as a deep river, swift borne, will take under willows near the bank.

My husband was only home at the week-ends. How we worked! We sorted, burned rubbish, planted, dug. The garden showed how rich it was by the strength and pugnaciousness of its weeds: the old cracked soil that dried to something like flagstones in a single day's sunlight was bound and netted by buttercups which grew while we tried to squeeze into the four-roomed cottage which was crammed with furniture too big for it, and too many books for it to digest. Slowly, laboriously we dusted, polished, planted. The result was the prettiest little cottage we ever lived in and one of the most feeding gardens.

[1] This is incorrect. The Miltonic sonnet is not the pure Italian in that it allows a freer and more liberal use of rhyme. Christina Rossetti's are Italianate sonnets.

CHAPTER IX

IT was called The Black House, for it was tarred outside. Some minute muslin curtains were made for the windows, the geraniums were set in them, the old black flagstones were polished, the coppers shone in the log-light of the open kitchen fire. The whole of the inside was painted a clear yellow, including the charming little old staircase.

It had a parlour like a nut. There were four rooms, an outdoor lavatory, a lean-to wash-house with an earth floor, and a pigscot. At the gateway stood an immensely tall pine. All its branches went up in the air except one, which it held stiffly out over the roof, in a commanding gesture. There were two ash trees of very interesting shapes in the field behind. I was always trying to draw them.

As I write it seems to me that I have only just gone to live there, not been *and* gone. And when we saw it as we did after we had left it, we could not take in the fact that it was no longer home, so many storms, mists, blizzards and snowstorms did it shelter us from.

For the air up there, though very, very pure, used to get involved with the clouds. At a thousand feet this will happen, particularly in winter. And it was never still. On the hottest day—we had but very few, for this was the summer of 1950—you could feel a little frill of breeze under your chin like a beard, and your hair alive. Everything, flower, leaf, vegetable, lamb and bird, came a month later than down below.

Spring came and late spring and poured over us such flowers, such flowering trees in wood and hedges. The may, the wayfaring tree for the lanes, for the gardens a little before, the forsythia that shows so well against grey stone. Our flowers began to show leaves above the earth.

PART II
THE OTHER SIDE OF THE WAVE

The Pioneer

That which in me came last
is now the first,
and has the bravest eyes:
he goes my mind before
and tramps unto the door
of yet unwelcomed skies.
Continuous, and adventurous
his way lies.

His footsteps' choice is snow,
nor will that creed allow
tomorrow's likely sun.
But for more glorious air
the dark his shoulders bear
and "space has just begun!"
he dogged cries.
For me the days are mist,
the climate too is lost.
"Is harvest tided;
Or is it spring that's near
ecstatically clear
its scent decided?"
He answers, "Where we go
the years are not divided."

"No flowers then rally there,
no breath, but only air?"
"No, truly none."
"So sure?
then I'll go with you Pioneer,
but you must hope alone."

CHAPTER I

THE experience of feeling, of observing Nature, is profoundly restful: as I have said, it is almost inevitable that in words the peace should be given out as strain. Intense solitude, in language, seems to descend to intensity. All Nature-writing will bear out this view: it is in Jefferies's *The Story of My Heart*, and it was inescapable in *Autobiography*, the work of a much less experienced writer. Only Thoreau, with his marvellous detachment, his cool interest in the economics of a natural life, was a completely successful Nature writer in prose: and even he was sufficiently puzzled by the medium of words to write his book topsy-turvy and back to front.

The person who faces the earth with a theory in his brain or a view in his eyes sees it without the quiet rapture of the devotee; but he is better equipped to describe what he *does* observe. In poetry, the language of passion, it is possible to convey a poet's delight in words which enchant without strain, for the reader comes to poetry prepared for ardour and also for eccentricity. There is much in Herbert's poetry to support this; and it is in all Wordsworth's finest poems.

I say I thought about a Creator of E——: but I thought about what I saw as I saw it first. Just as one reads the poems of Herbert and Vaughan one must read the earth—first for its loveliness and only secondly for its sacredness. That one does read poetry so, seems incontestable, or why are not ordinary hymns associated with beauty in our minds as the 'holy' poems of these poets are?

What *did* I see? I have destroyed all but one incomplete diary of that time. It was now the spring of 1950—the late spring of E——. As if from all channels and by all the rays of the sky centred upon my brain, impressions of the wide country, the animals, the insects that lived in it and the work of the house and garden, and my own self-created thoughts, rushed in upon me with an almost insufferable pressure. I had been amused by some criticisms of my work in which the critics detected unusually acute senses. I have not one acute sense unless it be my hearing: my eyes are very short-sighted, and through heavy smoking my sense of smell is dormant and restricted to such shouting smells as pigs, onions and curry. But my eyes lead directly into my brain. In a healthy person the body tires the brain, in one such as myself, the brain tires the body. Nothing I saw at that period *was silent*, but all spoke to me of themselves. It was like a great symphony which never ended, in which the instruments were running away with the music to disaster. The relaxation in the Earth, which was what I tried and failed to describe in *Autobiography*, was impossible to me now unless I lay back on the ground and shut my eyes. I was to regain it later, but only by dropping all attempts at writing of what interested me so much—the life of the woods and fields. I was to have to learn to take it commonly to pass and to forget what seems to me inspiration, delight and reason, to live in the countryside, as if it were a street. But not yet—first—the far side of the wave. How very often, standing on the shore, have I seen that high line of water coming in, and wondered what tidal bird, what face, what being, tossed beyond it, moving always, and always hidden? This is the mystery of the stormy sea, and the mystery of Consciousness, that one word for Time, Self and Response.

It was now May the tenth—the last day on my shore. I wrote in my diary that day and here is the entry:

'I'd been thinking about wickedness. Not refuting it, but asking if I am wicked does that mean I'm not necessary? And if we love or worship a quality, one quality, such as chastity say, or love or kindness, isn't it rather like loving one part of some one's body—the hair, or the hand, or the eyes? Or if one can imagine a part of God, worshipping that?

'To worship and accept the sum: that seems to me growth. After I'd eaten some scraps I went and lay down out of doors on the weeds. It was the first time this year heat had gathered on my skin—the leaf shadows were tossing like spray, the sky was blue all over, and the earth was dry on the spade. In the grass under the hedge a pair of enormous Roman snails, the colour of onions and with a grain like them in their shells, were stuck together, mating. Two large white butterflies in the air over the garden seemed now trying to weave themselves into a floral garland without enough flowers to make it, now to build a tower of Babel. I looked at the onion bed. Each onionling wore its tiny black seed on the top of the blade. It was like looking at the earth through a microscope on the moon. Oh Great Bach, oh great mild Stradivari, I feel an intuition towards you!'

The handwriting is strong and ordinary, the observation quite sound and acute it seems to me. There are no signs of an approaching crisis. And yet the next night I was to pass the wave, and this was the last writing I ever put down in the state of not being aware of being mentally affected by epilepsy. I was forty-two years old.

It was at night, on May the 11th, and the sonnet (for it was the rough start of one) is stained and nearly unreadable, but I was evidently still thinking on the same theme:

77

Oh you great men, great minds, great self-(expressed)[1]
I feel an intuition to you for you show
in piece, God's Manhood, and the God-(possessed)[1]
in men. All growth is God is all I know.

Earth pushes, heaven pulls and as we (illegible)[1]
the air, and stand at last full-grown (complete)[1]
the God in us ascends his own sublime
high character of love; and from its seat
over and in us calls us; and we bless
there in him all, and there too worship him
entire. Who dedicates his love to less
and loves for virtue only, one bright limb
of light alone adores, like a sunset branch.

It was on the night of May 11th I was writing thus. How
distinctly I remember it! Our cottage stood by itself, on
the lane side about a couple of hundred yards from our
nearest neighbours and friends who used to give us water
and were before and after my first attack so consistently
calm, kind and humane. The night was quiet and dark—
I went to the door and looked out once or twice. It was
about eleven o'clock when I put down my pen, feeling
suddenly tired and saying to myself that I could do no more
that night, so I would make a cup of tea and go to bed.
I made the tea, looked up at the clock—a strange chance—
saw that it was ten minutes past eleven. The next thing I
was still looking up at the clock and the hands stood at five
and twenty minutes past midnight. I had fallen through
Time, Continuity and Being.

My first thought was not that the clock had gone wrong,
but that I had been asleep. I discovered I was lying on the

---

[1] The stain of the spilt tea-cup.

floor on my back, my head against the rungs of a rocking-chair and my body, full length, crowded between the steel fender and the little table at which I had been writing. The lamp, a tall brass one, on a very slender base, was burning steadily on the table; always cold when sitting still, I had made up a large fire to work by and this was burning hotly in the open fireplace with wood and coal ablaze. It was not until much later on, appalled and shaken, I realized how dangerously I had been placed, unconscious, certainly in convulsions, in a locked cottage alone with my dog at midnight and a quarter of a mile from the village.

The space in which I was lying was perhaps a yard wide. My sleeve was charred by an ember, but this was all. Had some special agent of preservation laid me down between lamp and fire it could not have been more dexterously done. When despairing I have often recalled this to myself. My head was turned so that my opening eyes could not do otherwise than see the clock face. After a fit, the one unforgettable sight is the first thing one sees *consciously*. And this little green enamel alarm clock, our only time-piece, given to us ten years before for a wedding present, whose heart had ticked through so many solitary nights and evenings all through the war, became at once more than it had ever been, a memory and a reality. It frightened me for a moment, but only as the face of a friend who tells incomprehensible news. I simply stared at it. Then slowly mind and body began to try to come together and to work out a scheme for movement. It was the most difficult feat I have ever attempted, for *nothing* physical or mental was in unison, nor were they ready to fuse and to act for one body.

I must have turned my head, for the next things I saw were my dog's beautiful yellow eyes. They were fixed on me and she was lying in her basket. She looked calm; but as she saw me move, she relaxed her gaze, got up, and went and rummaged for her biscuits which I had put down for her under the table when I had made the tea.

It seems peculiar that I should have accepted the fact of lying there on the floor for in those times I never slept suddenly, neither would I have lain down so close to the flames. But I did. Any idea, however ready-made, seemed fit for me then. After a few moments with open eyes, lying still, I began to feel very ill, sick and faint. And then I can remember my mind beginning to work, for it told me I must be ill and must go to bed.

Then came an extraordinary blank. I had reached the idea, the image, of bed, but where *was* bed? The next mental process is terribly difficult to describe, for, as after, all my bad fits, the brain held and let go, held and let go, a confused mass of atmosphere and memory. It worked, but like an engine misfiring and unsteered. The idea of going to bed brought an extraordinarily vivid presentment of our childhood's room where I had slept with my sister, gone these many many years. I saw the blue distempered walls, the tallboy. This floated in my head and vanished, to be followed by every room I had ever slept in, *except the present one*. But going to bed, and not knowing where to go raised a much more acute question—*who was I*? I seemed to think this over but in a casual sort of way, even with a certain amusement. Another image was bobbing up and down in me, and again it was amazingly solid, was seen and then snatched away and then seen again as though held up in the air before me, as, I have since imagined, religious maniacs behold their sins. It was a jug, a blue-banded, quart milk-jug.

It was the jug roused me, for into it we always poured

our can of afternoon's milk, and I remembered that I hadn't done it. Conscience seemed to bring consciousness and strength. Conscience because the brain interrupted seems to work by precept; and it was one of my mother's housewifely rules which I had always followed to empty your milk at once so that the cream didn't stick to the can. None of these minute details are out of place—on the contrary they are important in revealing how the broken consciousness joins itself together again.

The whole of my experience of my first fit is as vivid and exact as this.

I got up from the floor noticing how the matting was wrunkled though the light of the single burner lamp was not bright except on the page where I had written my poem and the low ceiling.

I emptied the milk into the jug: and then feeling suddenly sick sat down on the stairs and retched. I was not sick, for it was hours since I had eaten anything: but then, fully roused, I was really frightened, for I can count my bilious attacks by decades and a half.

'I have eaten something that has disagreed with me, or I have been poisoned and fainted,' I thought. Troubled at there being no help I went outside the door for air. There were still curious numb patches in my thought and a feeling that the soul didn't know whither it had returned, to the right earth, or to an unknown one. As the air touched me I felt a cold dampness and it came on me stunningly, terrifyingly, that my clothes were wet. My urine had escaped me then. Horrifyingly, in one moment, I realized the incredible, impossible, and ghastly truth—I had neither fainted nor been asleep: I had had an epileptic fit! A fit, to a healthy woman, on whose ability to live alone so much depended! A horrible, perhaps incurable illness lay before me. Moreover I was alone and at any moment might have another.

Searching the room, I found everything confirmed my instantaneous certainty. The wet rug where I had lain, the lapse of time, no mere stutter in the consciousness this time, but a full hour and ten minutes, the stunned mind, all showed it had been a fit and a bad one. I saw now that my tea-cup had been upset all over the page obliterating part of the poem, and that stained page is before me now. I recollected that I could not remember drinking the tea, but only making it and filling the cup. The pot still stood on the hob. The chair I'd been sitting in to write was overturned and lying on its side. The table, so small, so slight that it could hold no more than the MS., the lamp and the cup, was not even moved. I think the miracle of the escape of us two living creatures from death by burning touched me even then, though there was no spiritual force in me to react to it.

Going over the room I told myself what had happened. I had fallen just as I was lifting the cup to drink, by the evidence. I had no memory of it. It had seemed as I have told—one moment filling the tea-pot and glancing at the clock, the next waking and still looking at the clock an hour later.

CHAPTER II

DURING my examination of the room I did not speak to my dog, nor make any noise. One loud groan came from me with the awful flashing revelation of the truth; and that I heard. My terror was that before help could be fetched I might go into another fit. Therefore, mind and body, now fused, and working clearly, with no feeling of illness or any near confusion, I began to make things as safe as I could while preparing to run to my neighbours. I acted quickly and briefly, as if I had become some swift, urgent story. The things I did are curious considering my fear of another imminent attack, for they need not have been done and show perhaps that mentally I was not as normal as I felt.

First I wiped the floor and changed my clothes completely. Then I thought of the milk in the blue-banded jug and took it out of the hot room. The fire I avoided—it was safe enough inside the fender anyhow—but I put out the lamp. Finally, locking the door I went up the lane with my dog by my side. It was then long past one in the morning.

It was exactly as if I had committed a murder and was determined to trim off the deed properly. In fact, one friend's comment to whom I told these details afterwards was, characteristically, 'What a terrible murderess you would make!'

My neighbours were asleep, the house dark, the whole bare earth around on the top of that long lonely hill was felt.

Relentlessly I knocked and banged on the door. When they came down, pale and sleepy, and saw me standing in the porch I just said, 'I have had a fit, I think. Will you ring up the college hostel and get M——'

I remember no more of that night distinctly. I had reached safety and shelter and kindness. There was no more danger. They took me in as if people banging them up in the middle of the night saying they had had seizures was a common occurrence. They put me to bed on their sofa, gave me hot tea and a hot water bottle, and got my husband. Then they put him to sleep beside me on a camp bed. I slept.

In the morning I asked Mrs. B—— if she had noticed anything strange about me. I knew her well, of course, after so many months and always called her Betty. She said:

'There was only one thing. You said Mrs. B——. And you were a queer yellowy-grey.'

The next day I spent in bed at the cottage and my husband had leave to stay with me. The doctor came— Dr. Y—— to whose care and Professor T——'s I owe my partial recovery and may owe the whole if I outlive this long-lived disease. He examined me. Found heart, lungs and all organs in proper order, and said he could not explain it.

'But I can,' I said, 'it was an epileptic fit.'

His only answer to that was: 'Why should it be?'

My conviction was and is that he knew at once. For he said to my husband in the garden: 'She knows too much.' And I do not think he said it in derision. If he had only been acquainted with the circumstances of my childhood, living so near this large epileptic colony, and only a few months before returning to that neighbourhood of afflicted people, he would have been certain that mine was no hysterical diagnosis, little right as I had to make it to any one but myself.

He was all patience, thoroughness, good humour towards that annoying type of patient who declares his own disease to his doctor. And he prescribed luminal. And made an appointment for me to be seen by Professor T—— at the Neurological Institute near Clystowe as soon as possible. Meanwhile his advice was to take the luminal and go on the same as usual. In Clystowe Professor T—— would tell me one way or the other and they would make an electro-encephalograph (a chart of the brain). Just to wait.

Just to wait.

The appointment was for June the 8th.

To wait. To wait.

And now, I whose mental processes had been so un-cannily accelerated for years, whose imagery was so urgent, overcrowded, like an orchestra choked with instruments, had to spin out thoughts as a curtain against fear and horror. Fear of the yet unexperienced cycle of the pits, the intervals between them, horror of myself.

Every waking was a shock and an enigma: 'Is this myself? Is it a nightmare?'

I was so sure I used to tell myself every morning as soon as I woke: 'You are an epileptic.' For the rest of the day I would protest and try to believe that I was not. Thus I was prepared for either truth, like all cowards. For surely one of those two, the day or the awakening, I owned and must soon confess myself to be.

'Just go on as usual.' And we did. My husband had gone back to sleep at the College hostel and was home at the week-ends only. What to *do*? Life was my waiting-room.

Just as in Ireland, my headaches, dizziness and much of my mental velocity was gone. Indeed, since having the major fits these have never returned. The disease absorbed its own triviata—they vanished into it, as they had into happiness, enjoyment and liberty a year before.

I expected to be a different person, just as if I had committed a great crime or been converted to a sexual perversion. I found myself unchanged. Except for the fear which made me stop and tremble all over as I had on the night of the fit itself.

In spite of an inner certainty to which it was necessary to confess once a day, I argued against its having been epilepsy. The morning after the fit, on combing my hair I had found a cut an inch long at the base of my head at the back, evidently done in falling backwards on to the steel edged fender. Could that have caused the incontinence, I asked the doctor? No, he said, it would not account for that, though if I had knocked myself out, it might for the length of time I lay unconscious. The fit, then, I told myself, might not have been a very bad one. If the cycle were a wide enough one—i.e. the intervals between the attacks far enough apart—it might be a bearable affair altogether. I was strong, I was usable, I was in no pain and I found the earth as enigmatically wonderful as ever. There is, however, a strong morbid or puritanical tendency in me; this would tell me that I had committed some wrong, some mistake, in my past life, for which I had to pay compensation. It might be an ethical sin, or a spiritual one, or an artistic one. My belief fastened finally on the last. It was the only interpretation: mentally I had defrauded my brain by physically occupying myself. I had broken the philosophical and artistic principles of the only philosopher in whom I ever believed—Henry David Thoreau. It was our possessions, our equipment which had brought us to this—dusting books and polishing old furniture and even planting more vegetables than we could eat in a winter. Few as our possessions were compared with many people's, they were far, far too much for use or even for delight. And I remembered my old wish for no more equipment except thoughts. It seemed to me that those possessions we cannot share either with God or our spirits in which God is, are hateful and injurious.

'I must start again on my Emily Brontë book. I must do something to keep myself calm and decent,' I wrote in my diary.

I could not settle to gardening but lay on the grass with my MSS. In vain the cabbage butterflies lifted themselves like white admonitory fingers. The weeds started to grow. The yellow-hammers grew hardy and perched near me, letting out their little beggarly cries: 'A-little-bit-of-bread-and-*no*-cheese,' and the little bird that is like a tiny forge and reminded me of our own home village and brook, clanged in the ivy.

Meanwhile I took such precautions as I could. I put a guard on the fire, and on the week-day nights when I was alone I went to bed in daylight, to avoid the danger of a lamp.

'None is so poor that he need sit upon a pumpkin,' wrote Thoreau. None is so frightened that he need fix his eyes on Fear by day and by night, though I made a kind of companion of it as Thoreau did of the blizzards.

There was a long coast of large beech trees, edging one of the huge, empty grass fields, having within their line the stumps and weeds of another broken wood. Here, if I left the cottage, I used to walk, and listen to the new leaves in the wind. Had I been a Thoreau I might have pondered on the mistakes of keeping too much company or spending too much money. Had I been a Richard Jefferies put out towards those great trees and that June high air the religious faith in physical well-being which irradiates *Bevis* and *The Story of My Heart*. I did feel that they breathed out health and strength: during the month that passed between my fit and its definition by Professor T——. Earth *did* once again interpose its shoulder between suffering and myself. I never thought I should have a fit out of doors, and I never have. Since there is, I have been assured by him, no neuromimetic tendency in me to aggravate the disease, it must be assumed that walking and breathing freshness and being quiet, above all, does something to the system which tones it and tunes it. And that far from being morbid as Mr. Savage suggested and I am sure genuinely thought, my long passion for earth-life and its study, was as healthy and protective, as spiritual, as any religion could be. For there I was alone, yet not alone, peaceful yet not stagnant, stimulated yet relaxed. That unity between what many call inanimate Nature, and the being of a human creature, was never so apparent as it was to me then. I remembered *Man*, the greatest, the most mystic and the most prophetic of all Herbert's poems, and knew through it as through the leaves:

"He is in little all the Sphere;
Herbs gladly cure our flesh because that they
find their acquaintance there . . .

For as the winds do blow;
the Earth doth rest, Heaven move, and fountains flow;
Nothing we see but means our good
as our delight or as our treasure . . ."

88

Yet, though the health of spring and of all growth helped me, it was never to be quite the same. Death, more death, had entered me through unconsciousness, as it partly had the year before through grief, and the first hint, years before, through a moment of recorded ecstasy. Sometime, after youth, Death will make its entrance as Thought and will remain. The hope of it came to Emily Brontë years before she died: Emily Dickinson changed places with it while a young woman and leapt out of living while alive with the astounding poem:

"'Twas just this time last year I died . . .'

making mere forecast timid, and prophecy pale. Perhaps the best and least contradictory account of my state I can give is from some pages in my diary. The date is May 19th.

'*May 21st*. The rain came one day, delicately trotting on the leaves. Hedges, trees, fields, road borders grew green as moss and the cuckoo spoke.

'Upstairs in the bedroom under the rafters I listen to the muslin sound of it, entranced as always by the summery shadow of the shower.

'Then to-day we had a long thunderstorm, a terrible sky. Rosie and I were wet and I ran in throwing my load of wood down in the flooding garden. Lit the lamp not to see the flashes, but saw them, and heard the awful noise of the thunder up the open chimney. It made my head worse and it has been bad enough since the fall that night.

'After it was over I looked out of the window upstairs and saw the low, long, tiny blue world of distance, blue as the sea, lying under the banded clouds, and the light returned to the sky. All the weight of the storm had rolled over to the western side, like a pain that crosses the body. And with the light the flowers and leaves began to dance and

89

sway and the birds to call out. And now it darkens again—
the window chills. . . . Yesterday in the garden I did a
little work. I was moving a heap of rotten cabbage stalks
and found underneath a mother mouse with three young
ones. She was a pretty creature, tawny-skinned, with very
small terrified eyes, and a paralysed or else non-existent
maternal instinct. The babies had their fur and tiny dim
eyes, and ran off in all directions while she, squeaking
loudly, burrowed her face under a leaf. I waited, and as
the babies and the mother at last crouched down and kept
perfectly still with their wee eyes shut I was able to pick
them up and put them to her and then hastily build a sort
of cabbage stalk and grass shanty over them. The truth is
that if Mother Mouse hadn't made such a fuss and shrieking
I should never have noticed any of them. It is always
interesting to see small life close-to, but I shall never
enjoy crushing or tearing or violating any of the small
nests, tubes, lairs and runs of insects and little animals
because it makes one feel one's weight and careless clumsi-
ness. To have been Goliath must have been a sad existence.
And one can never repair the secret lacework of the bee,
the caterpillar and the moth. Bee-keeping taught me that.

'*May 22nd*. I have a hope that it will help to straighten
out the disorder in me if I write down such things as mice
and thunderstorms. The outer life. For I am possessed by
restlessness and vacancy. I can't read and I feel too confused
to write. I have done myself more harm than I can undo
quickly. My physical rhythm is naturally as slow as my
mental capacity is fast. I cannot move quickly or act
quickly without rushing. To keep the workaday pace of
other people I have to hurry, hurry, hurry all the time and
even then I cannot keep up. The attempt has harmed me:
if I have hastened my slow body it does not matter, it is

only tired; but as you cannot separate the body from the brain, the continual hurrying of deeds has acted on me mentally and put to a greater speed thoughts and nervous instincts which were perhaps from the beginning abnormally rapid. *I am sure this is true.* This is why I cannot think coherently. My brain is like a roundabout whose music, roaring its loudest tune, is least distinct; whose gilt and coloured fables whirl so fast that there is no clear contour or shine but only a cloud of colour . . .

'*May 23rd*. Of Nature again . . . perhaps the discovery of God has undone my innocence. For there is no religious belief, no *modern* religious belief which at once contains and worships the earth, though most religions bid us watch the stars and consider their Maker, consider the sparrows and their Creator. Far from being able to watch the stars, religion (modern) will not have us bind our eyes to this one planet and its phenomena. I don't know therefore in what Faith I could enclose my solitary response to ordinary common Nature, unless within the ancient Jewish faith or the great Symbolical plurality of the old Greeks. That is, what is known to me of either. Of the old Jewish faith, as disclosed in the Old Testament, it seems clear by description and implication, that a great pastoral passion was enclosed within it, so illuminated is every historical, prophetic and poetic Book by the imagery of an old people whose every ultimate idea of beauty, peace and benignity was conveyed by illustrations from the beautiful in Nature. The beautiful, the noble, the enormous, the fearful, beginning from the Garden of Eden, all are from Nature. In Job, the greatest of all poems, God's argument of His own being is His creation of the world, His praises in the psalms also: the times of harvest, the times of tempest, the habits of beast and insect, all are pictures used to admonish or to illuminate the soul of man. These people must indeed have observed their world! There was a time, not more than a few years ago, when the air, the sky, all the natural vision of the earth and its tribes was such a picture of me to myself. The earth was as myself. It is not quite so now. Sometime—I don't quite know when—the separation happened. I have never been so happy since and don't expect to be so happy again, while alive, on earth.

'On Earth. The part of my spirit that broke away from life, broke away from me, and flew away, beyond, and seems to call to me to go after it. To renounce in spirit, if I cannot in fact, all possessions.

'I know that that is so. That something in me is demanding *its share of death*: and through all my natural and normal fears when death does indeed seem possible, that distant demand, this cry for the experience, sounds profoundly and insistently. It is as though the spirit knows it can't become acquainted with God here.

'Ultimately it is hope, not fear, which makes me think of death. Perhaps I am not going to have a long life; and so this feeling, which is only healthily appropriate to age, is right for me. It would be if I were having my folding years now.

'I don't think a lot about the other night now. The horror has certainly passed. I don't think it was a fit—oh I don't know! it might have been. But whatever it was physically—and it was total blackness, a hole in the self— to me, it was a glimpse. Some have them in visions, some in prayers, some come to them through entreaty, through disappointment, or weariness, some through sainthood. Death is the soul's delight, Death is God, Death grows to be our daily appetite. Give us our necessity.

'All I am sure about is the naturalness of it—at least the naturalness to people like me. For my body was to me my little earth: as the revelation of natural life and death was given to me through the great earth, so my little earth may reveal to me its storms and physical complexes, the mystery of its cessation.

'What do I mean by a glimpse? Nothing was seen. No, it was just the act of separation from the will, so entire, so instantaneous, so involuntary, that seemed to illustrate for me what is inevitably to come to be.

'To return to the humdrum of life is strange, is even sad. Food, drink, light, darkness, never completely satisfying again. They tire even: life *does* pall on the soul. The body *does* bore and weary. My mind would like to go free!

'For several days afterwards if I turned my head quickly, something, some unusual, some significant shape seemed just to avoid me, just to run out of the corner of my eye. There was always a sense—a visual sense—of collision averted by another form than my own. There was always that sense of quick movement, of transformation. Maybe it would be a stone, a post, which just one breath ago had been a human shape, a ghost. The world was populated with vanishings. It was queer, but sight itself haunted me like a thing half forgotten already, so quick is the spirit to learn a future which it has only *rehearsed* as it were, in a few unconscious moments.[1]

'*May 24th*. I have been to Cheltenham. Missed one bus back and had to wait an hour. The plane trees growing out of the ground where the country buses start have hard wiry roots above the hard earth, that spread like hens' feet. I don't know why, but as I waited a poem began to come to me, so I dashed into an antique shop and begged the lady for a paper and pencil.

[1] I was quite alone in the cottage during all these weeks except at week-ends before I saw Professor T——. There was only my dog with me.

'She looked at me quickly, so I said, "It's a poem."

'"Oh be quick—here you are!" she said. "They come to me like that too—"

'And she put them into my hand.

'I sat on the ground and wrote:

Love

'Tenderer water than the warmest rain
shall wash your hands,
and softer than the hayseed grass
love on your hair and face will pass
going to his melancholy lands
of pain.

Pray that not out of his fingers
one touch shall fall:
Nor that one footstep grow
where all should go.
Pray most that not with his angry all
he lingers.

Free is the unowned pleasure
as the passing farms
are free of the traveller.
Songs leave the reveller;
and sheaves shall not bind your arms
nor treasure.

The Blush

'Was it the hope or memory of his kiss
that stung her face so crimsonly
with a red thought, as gardens must
follow the bee?

94

Or was there felt a foottread, known,
upon the soft arterial root
earth barely covers, and the sea
under a lover's foot?

Or did the daylight blood arise
from its home heart, and to the cheek
fly to engulf him downward as the sun
drowns shadow from a scarlet peak?

'These two lyrics pleased me because they showed that
there is still something unexpected in me I can write.'

On this ends the extracts from my diary. On May 22nd
I had begun to write and re-write my book on *Emily
Brontë* having rough drafted the headings many times. My
hope was that through the darkness which had befallen me
I might see her more clearly. But it was not to be so. We
had one week of still, hot weather, before that disastrous
flooded summer at E—— when whole fields rotted, and
I used to go out every morning with my MSS. under the
pine tree and lie on the grass.

The extracts from my diary and note-books will show
how brief my jottings had become—a change indeed from
the winter before. With the attempt at creative and critical
writing the fatal voluminousness began again. I could in
no way control the ideas which streamed in upon me as if
from the outermost circle of my universe. They came as
if from all points and could not be focussed upon the
figure of the woman I was seeking to interpret, herself
universal. I felt that I understood the experience she had
undergone, which too was a circle having as its centre,
death. But in trying to put this understanding into words
I merely reproduced more circles of my own. And the few
dominant, dead personalities who had been in my life such

profound influences and interests protruded also into her life—or rather her work, as I saw it. They were very few: in a world directed by many thousands of geniuses and gods who have moulded the mass of mankind, my interest has ever been confined to a very small number. The writings of Thoreau, of Byron, of Herbert and Vaughan, and in more modern times of Lawrence and Jefferies, became more and more analogous: the music of Bach, Beethoven, Handel and Mozart, interwoven with their human and divine lives, obtruded where there could be no certain connection but one of a mind disturbed. And the suffering of Jacob Stainer and John Clare seemed to augment all mankind's.

In this attempted critical work I seemed to be trying to write an essay on man—I who know no philosophy, no language but English, and very little history or religion! I could find no up-to-date vehicle for my thoughts: agree with Emily Brontë's greatness and her death I must; for she alone of all the women I had read seemed to have grasped the importance of dying. Yet, I would argue, in writing, was her death so important: has not martyrdom been summed up once and for all by Thoreau's life and his belief that it is easier to die for death than to live for life? So that as I wrote on those hot mornings, with the thick dew drying off the grass like the chill off an iced glass, it was inevitable that I should become more and more antagonistic to Emily Brontë as a human soul; and should involve my pen in more arguments every day in favour of the spiritual superiority of her two less wonderfully gifted sisters Charlotte and Anne. Their writings with their simpler, aching revelation of real human hearts undeflected by highest genius, suffering the pain of grief and separation seemed to me more and more moving, hers, so distant in the ether, less so. For I had an inkling of her consolations, in them I found none. I was beginning to value the human being.

I am sure now that during the month before I saw Professor T—— shock and fear, and the presence of Nature like an angel too near, had unbalanced my mind, and in waking, like water, it revealed both amount and depth which I had never known existed in me. Thought, profound thought, underlay the simplest and the smallest thing. But it was always egoistic thought: i.e. thought existing from something to myself, or from myself to something or somebody else. Half of my universe is myself—that is too much. One is not, or should not be, half of a lifelong conversation with the world, but sometimes a silent witness. Ideas which exist between ideas, which balance like cobwebs across the human structure, from abstract points, or from many intellects apart from oneself or one's immediate urgent impulses, are part of the brain's balance. I knew my egoism to be harmless, since I was bound myself to be aware that my life among the people I loved, and the people I knew had not been all a selfish one. I had worked and I had done without a certain amount. But privation of the self from the self is no better than privation of the individual by any one else and that I still believe. Yet I began to see that I was not free, that I was indeed in chains to my brain, and even hopelessly and despairingly involved with it and I began to ask: 'Is epilepsy a religious or a moral disease? Is it possible that it is my *fault*?'

CHAPTER III

AND here I must re-quote Mr. Custance's significant paragraph on his experiences as a manic-depressive which have certainly been mine as an epileptic.

'I cannot, however hard I try, get even my most intimate relations and friends to understand or take any interest in what may or may not have happened to me during my "madness."'

This was my experience exactly, though my friends were not unbelieving as was my family, thank God, or I should have been in a poor way indeed. One cannot blame this attitude. It is natural that one's blood relations should not welcome a disease such as epilepsy into their circle. They are bound to protest against the idea of it, and to offer every solution of their own, however incredible, rather than accept the simple one. The piteousness of the battle between the convinced and convicted sufferer and those who may love him deeply, and yet now must fear the animosity of his symptoms, is a profoundly miserable affair. Why seek to convince them? If possible, it would be wiser not, but in my case help was needed, not indeed at once but later. I was convinced but not yet convicted.

Lack of perception was inevitable. We wrote letters. All parties showed obstinacy, myself prematurely, but not as it turned out mistakenly. I was accused of over-smoking, of affecting my heart and told that my attack was a faint resulting from this.

I have always smoked as hard as I could and more than I

could afford, the cause again of pecuniary hostility, always latent in families. But though I have never been completely unconscious before, except from anaesthetics, I had been close enough to it to be absolutely sure that one did not faint as I had fallen. There was a sinking away, a sick feeling, and a remembrance of it afterwards. One did not just come round with no conscious preliminary memories.

My letters grew angrier and angrier at the kindly meant advice in those I received. For from the beginning some inner watcher told me: accept, receive, habituate yourself. And I was not so stupid in psychological processes as not to see self-protection in the disbelief. They knew no more than I whether epilepsy was likely to attack several people in a family, or whether it was isolated in myself. If it were what I felt it to be, that I would tell them honestly when I had asked Professor T——. Meanwhile inexpert opinion, disbelief and the wrong sort of kind advice was irritating me and making me nervously furious. How grateful I was to my neighbours the B——s I could not even express to myself, for their quiet, good, waiting attitude. They seemed to me people without fear and without embarrassment. With them I was not shy of it happening again. And shyness more than fear was my first reaction to the disease. When you have always gone here and there alone, on your own feet, about your own thoughts and your own business, a spectacle to draw no one's attention, you do not like the idea of falling down and rolling about like an animal. It is horribly repugnant. Even more horrifying was the idea of coming round alone and finding the stamp of your animalism all around you, with no one to welcome you to yourself again and to introduce you to the life which had turned its back on you.

I was only at ease with the B——s and my husband. In
them my trust was folded and with them I could relax the
vigilance, the sharp, seeking gazes which in spite of all
efforts to be natural, *would* question everything around
me: 'Are you as you were, or have I departed from you
again?'

They, only, gave me back my sense of continuity.

It is true that as ever I would forget everything the
moment I began to write. But this was not for long.
After the fine hot week was over, I could no longer
struggle against the study I had been attempting. Then
the B——s would have me there, or would come in to
tea with me and we would sit in the kitchen eating
shortbread and heavy cake while Major B—— told us about
the ancient layout of the village and tales of squires and
ruins.

And I found a wonderful comfort and stability in an
old friend who lived in Gloucester—Mrs. S—— who lived
alone with a bad heart. A clever literary person would
perhaps have said of this friend's methodist Christianity
that she had God in her pocket or some such. Perhaps, I
used to think, the pocket was her heart. To other people
I told myself, I must not continue to write, and if I could
not convince them that I had not just had a faint or some
vague 'neurotic attack'—the word was theirs, not mine,
I must leave it so.

At night when the fears were nearest, and my book
untouched for days, seemed to spread and spread its un-
rolling thoughts before me on the candle-light, I would
play that I was a child and write in my diary:

'On some such lovely morning, full of sun and thick
dew, with waving branches, I'd get up and run down alone
to the river and swim in the warm, heavy current that

seemed tepid after the early air. The farm, Aunt Fran and Uncle Donaven. The fields and the cows asleep. I was fourteen. People dead and me old. Never swim again on a summer morning, in youth.'

And when I lay in the bed alone I imagined myself a child and to-morrow would be Christmas Day or my birthday. Dad and Mother were as we first had them. Many nights I went to sleep *being this*.

Once I almost saw my father when he came home in the evening from 'the office.' He came upstairs and bent over me and gave me Beatrix Potter's *Tom Kitten*. 'Here is your book,' I heard him say. And saw again for the first time the delicate little home pictures of that delicious master-piece in its transparent paper-cover. And then I went to sleep. My treasure was mine. What he had promised to me he had brought me.

On June the 8th I went to be seen by Professor T—— at the Neurological Institute. I could remember every detail of that day, even if it were not written in my diary, under the characteristically dramatic heading of 'The Lonely Journey.'

It began sadly. A very hot day was beginning and as I shut the cottage gate a big car flew past me up the lane, blowing me aside like a curtain.

When I reached the cross-roads my friend Mrs. B——'s beautiful tabby cat was dead on the road. I stopped only a moment to tell them and hurried on, for it was a mile to the bus which would carry me into Cheltenham to catch the long-distance coach. But I heard my friend crying because the cat was her child's and a favourite and it had seemed so cruelly unnecessary.

In Clystowe the heat was thundery, the traffic to me seemed insane and impulsive beyond fathoming, and my head was aching very badly. I had my luminal in my pocket but would not take any.

The Neurological Institute is a few miles out of Clystowe in the country. Tired and dulled by headache, with that tautness as of the skin which comes over people about to enter a health institute and face a strange specialist, I have nevertheless not often experienced such velocity of thought as on the short journey by bus to the turning. Soul or Spirit, or integral being, whichever the true self is, had left me; and only the mental processes remained. My brain seemed all over my body. It reflected on music and the art of conveying music through instruments and the touch on strings or keyboard, such as the fact that greater physical strength is needed to reserve power than to use it, and the true pp. is power folded small, as in the bud of a flower but expandable to the utmost that hearing can endure— it is not shrunken touch but potential. Then I thought of Thoreau's face on which the forests grew when he was dead, then of Isaac Newton in his low, quiet house, watching the earth with all his brain in his eyes: then of Faith and disbelief. I asked myself whether it could be possible to be born believing—that is truly believing not from words inwards, but inwards outwards towards words; or whether to believe in God one must first disbelieve, which was an old question to me. And it seemed to me the most vital of all, and the reason why, although not sufficiently obsessed to think the religious poets greater than Shakespeare, they must always be more interesting to the person one is than that tremendous entertainer and interpreter of humanity, within whose immense intellect philosophy was religion. For within the great religious poet, whether it be David, Donne, Herbert, Vaughan, Baudelaire, there is, whether consciously or unconsciously, not only Faith but counter-faith: and the struggle, called by them Sin, or Sins, is what the ordinary soul suffers in life and what illustrates it to itself as it absorbs the poem.

In short, the invaluable disbelief it expresses may fit it a great deal more easily than the Declaration or Faith. It seems in most of these poets that a great deal of the evil of which they accuse themselves is, in various disguises, nothing more than natural incredulity. Thus in the best of them one discovers not only the beauty of Nature interpreted, but the whole of the human soul as Nature and God invented it. Disbelief is hardly a lesser revelation than belief and is as famous an inventor and investigator of causes. The greater psalms, the poems greater in meaning though perhaps not in beauty, contain all this element of unrest. Herbert, to preserve his faith and his enthusiasm for his creed, had to pass a chain about his thoughts as I have seen one girdle a tottering tree trunk, and spoke of 'wantonness in contemplation' in the poem *Content* which opens with

> Peace, muttering thoughts, and do not grudge to keep
> Within the walls of your own breast.

Certainly the incredulity (incredulousness?) of a truthful mind is a fine trait: and should surely not be repressed in order to make soul's history outwardly perfect and all of a pattern. But, now, when the bus stopped at the foot of a hill in the bright fields, I was face to face with my own stale dilemma. I remember a black pony, glossy in his summer coat, standing under some bushy old trees in a little paddock, switching the flies off his haunches with his long tail and wondering what should be *my* certainty when I next saw him in his. And a car coming down the hill bashed a chestnut leaf to the road which I picked up and held all the time they were binding the machine on to my head (the electro-encephalograph) and taking the first electro-encephalogram of my brain. I lay there holding the green thumbless hand of the leaf while things clicked and machinery came to life, and commands to gasp, to open and shut my eyes, reached me from across the unseen room, as though by wireless. Lights like comets dangled before me, slow at first and then gaining a fury of speed and change, whirling colour into colour, angle into angle. They were all pure ultra unearthly colours, mental colours, not deep visual ones. There was no glow in them but only activity and revolution.

When this was over I was shown into Professor T——. This man of international reputation, this great detective of neurotic diseases, looked like a detective of fiction, so straight and sheer a glance came from his eyes. The room in which he sat was furnished with him, with papers, a large window, a desk and two chairs, one of which I was ordered to take—it contained besides a mystery for me and its solution in those eyes.

Professor T—— was tall, strong and old. He did not like me, not that that mattered to either of us: neither was it surprising. I answered him baldly, told him almost nothing and made several remote mistakes in institutional etiquette. I liked him immensely and at once trusted him and admired the manner in which he spoke to me of my illness. I suppose that my lack of response was shock or headache or the real fear I felt of taking up too much of so important a person's time.

He spoke outright, as all strong people do, free of death and life and the body. He said he had no doubt whatever that it was epilepsy, dormant perhaps during most of my life, and breaking out at last in this major fit of a month ago.

Then came the questions I had expected and had fitted into this new idea of myself during the time I had been alone since the fit. Had I ever had any dizzy attacks, anything, however brief, of the kind which was like a very short break of consciousness? I answered yes, but I had always supposed that all people had these experiences sometimes.

'No,' said the Professor, 'they don't. Those were minor fits. Can you remember how long you have had them?'

I thought: 'Perhaps since I was about nine. My memory begins so late that it is hard to say.'

Had I ever had an accident or a fall? As a child, I replied, our mother had been exceptionally careful of us and it was unlikely. But I *could* remember falling off a pony when I was learning to ride. And this is the second of my coincidences of which the first was my having two minor attacks on one spot of ground near a wood which was for me connected with very powerful and (for a child) tragic emotions. We were taught to ride by our cousin, a fine horsewoman, and our uncle always watched the saddling of the pony himself. One day seeing that the safety catch of the near stirrup was rusty, he ordered that it should be left down or open, in case we might fall and be dragged on the leather by the catch failing to act. On that day and the next coming proudly down the paddock at a gallop, the leather slipped of its own accord through the open catch: and I was flung hard on my back and the back of my head, in exactly the same part of the field. I was not even giddy from the fall, but this was the only accident to my head I could recollect.

The Professor enquired into my family history: finding

it quite clear on both sides he said that although it was very, very difficult to find a cause for epilepsy even among those who knew most about it as it is one of the most mysterious and elusive diseases, he thought that I must have a slight scar on the brain from an old injury.

'It is very slight. Even if I could examine your brain I doubt if I could see it,' he said. 'But it is there, and at certain times it might hold up the circulation of the blood in the brain and you would have a fit. Other people would just feel irritable—you have a fit.'

I gathered that the cause of my epilepsy was much slighter than its symptoms—that it was, in fact, nothing to worry about and that it was very unlikely that any other person in my family would develop it.

'You may never have another,' Professor T—— said. 'You will have to take medicine. And *you will take it*? It is surely not too much trouble to remember to take some tablets? I will write to your doctor.'

I said it was certainly not. And I thought that this cross, clever man had so sweet and sudden a smile that it was a pity I had so little about me to provoke it. And I walked out of the Institute as a person harbouring epilepsy, it was true, but free of false hopes and quite clearly defined as myself by another person's firmness, directness, courage and knowledge. These benefits, sureness and determination to help oneself, are a part of Professor T——. It was not until later, after seeing him several times when it was no longer necessary for him to draw so tight a line round my vagueness, that I began to understand his own elasticity, his imaginative power, his *likeableness* as distinct from his achievement, and to comprehend the feeling of ease and sympathy I had felt in the presence of a man so eminent. He is a man who uses his personality on and for his patients as all who deal with brain disorders must: but he is a man who, not easily within reach, mentally existed, I felt sure, as I did, with himself. A rare man, a man without loneliness, as I was without it.

This sense of courage and of clarity is the professor's healing to his patients. He can renew it: and it needs renewing. Once away from his direct words, the belief he has conveyed is attacked by the world in its ignorance and hatred of the sick. 'If you can't be well, get out of my sight,' is the natural if unexpressed reaction of the healthy to the unhealthy. If we could only see ourselves dying probably we should be neither afraid of it nor unpitying. But how many of us are self-satisfied with our health as with our houses, cars, front gardens, etc. A person's reaction to death, not to life, is the true measure of his mental type: contrary to religion's—'lull life, but waken death. Life needs lullabies, not death,' but it is religions which try to make death sleep, or to disguise it and make it wholesome, like flowers lining a grave. The animals abominate and abhor it, or if they are tame and know it will be removed, are extraordinarily indifferent and apathetic.

I come to this obsession with death again because during the months from June 8th to October, when I had my second attack, it returned. I had never really thought until then that I myself was going to die soon, but now I did. I cannot think why, for I was perfectly well aware that people do not die of fits.

CHAPTER IV

THE questions I had dreaded had all been answered by what I dreaded. From that minute I realized how little hope was mine, when the reaction to certainty was so faint. I did not after all feel any different from before, as on my way home I passed the indolent black pony still switching flies like John Clare sitting in the ditch all day.

The period which followed for me saw little alteration either in our circumstances or mentally. My husband, owing to the Professor's letter to the college authorities, came home every night so that I was no longer alone after dark with the danger of candles and lamps. I began my regular night and morning doses of the prescribed drugs, luminal and epinutin. Their first effect was to create in me a latent sleepiness which the least caress of casual rest or even a stroke of sunshine on me, called out; it was a physical reaction—my brain remained awake and was often *actively meditating* within a body that was like a stone in the sun. There was, however, a big difference in these peculiar introverted egoistical posing and mental answering of questions, and in my hierarchy of images. It was as though, in having that first major fit, something hidden which had animated what was *not* hidden in my thoughts, had exploded and left them more true to their real character; as if also, in declaring the disease and speaking simply as he had, Professor T—— had sprung a spring. I am as sure as one can be of one's own symptoms that this return to a more normal and relaxed condition was not drug-induced unless the influence of a guiding personality is a drug, which of course it may be.

My Cheltenham doctor became our great friend and could not have been kinder or more careful: with him we did not speak of the disease unless I had an attack. And I did not have one during the whole of that summer. I went, in fact, three months and had forgotten the fact of the disease being within me when the next fit happened.

I was still by myself all day from about eight o'clock onwards. The hours went as they always had, in housework, gardening, roaming the fields and woods with my dog, and going in and out of my friends the B——s' home. It was during this wet summer too that I came to know the village and its people. My diary during this time is full of nature notes and country gossip. I made red currant jelly, I painted a careful study of the white campion and the wild geranium. The colour of these last flowers lit the lanes all the summer with a light like the flame of methylated spirit. I noted that they were 'fragile flowers, prolific but brief, dropping thousands of petals in a night, and next morning opening thousands of their dark anemone-like buds.'

Their coral spears and spurs bewitched the eye.

Then there were the Roman snails. 'Their mystery and breeding fascinates me,' I wrote: 'those pale enormous onion-brown shells, those opaque slow fleshes and the complete, calm, segregated existence of them, ancient and silent and still.'

My friends the B——s told me that these monsters were the true unchanged descendants of the snails cultivated by the Romans for eating. I never discovered what particular food had sustained them so historically and so faithfully, but being taken one day by Dr. Y—— to see the Roman villa at Chedworth, the first sight that met us was one single solemn giant in the middle of the smoothed turf. I was told that wherever the Romans had settled in that countryside were found these snails, and the true Deadly Nightshade, a most majestic herb, never seen by me before.

Some agricultural spray, some modern lotion against pests was, however, killing them off. One day, in part of a wheatfield I found hundreds dead, and rotting in the shells. Then farther from the wall of corn and nearer the hedge the living ones again. And once we picked one up that had laid an egg: 'the egg was white and milky and perfectly round, like a globule of boiled tapioca seed.'

Then in the middle of such notes I find now brief incomprehensible mental ejaculations, to which the key is lost.

'The black currants were ripe, the moon was thin, the summer house door was ajar . . . would I rather be me, sane, in the secret way Ophelia was? And like Ophelia, dragging wild flowers with her through the dew? But I didn't touch them—the mallow, the ox-eye, the—oh, I forget words.'

Of course I remember that garden though, and where I was. We took a holiday and stayed at St. Ides with my sister, and it was the house where my mother was born, empty now and to be sold. And I remember going up to the door and ringing the bell, thinking it would take me back. And how I frightened my husband one evening by looking at him through a window with my solitary, not my company face. I changed the look a moment too late and then let it stay on, careless, and thinking that wisdom is used to muffle wisdom. I remembered my grandfather's black broadcloth, my grandmother's black dresses, and there was I, standing in their conservatory, roped with their vine. Some one had forgotten to air it, and the big bunches of grapes were covered with silver mould. It hurt me that it was to be sold when I had only just got back to it. And I was never so tired in my life. It was becoming impossible to hide the fact that I could hardly lift my feet all day from the ground. With a curious certainty that there were but two possibilities and that my body, which was as secret to me as a black forest, had already chosen one, I said to myself that I was either very ill indeed or was going to have a child.

I would pull up some of the tall weeds in the dissolving garden that were already enfolding its colours in their general grey-green clouds, and then exhausted, sit on the brick steps of the Victorian summer-house. Once I took my violin, Jacob, into the empty house and filled it with long, uncertain ugly echoes that seemed in some strange way to prolong and to draw forth the memories of those who had lived there. It will be seen that I had plenty of time to ruminate and to ask questions of my certainty. If I were ill, that explained the feeling that death was about me: if with child, the stirring of faint emotions not yet sensations, within the physical being—emotions whose faint potency resembled, I thought, the dim step of the genius walking through the great edifice whose empty proportions he is to alter and enrich with his hands. So might a great renaissance painter move under a dome, gazing upwards, where he will presently lay his clouds, his angels and saints; or more truly a sculptor sense with his eyes the surface to be hollowed: there was as yet of course no touch, but only a regarding.

I did not know if epilepsy were likely to be inherited by my child; but though I thought of that it was without really strong distress, for I was too tired then to notice even so horrible a possibility. But another figure who had been one of my hierarchy of images seemed to move forward from her shadow—the figure of the Princess Cassandra, seer and virgin, beloved of Apollo, and cried aloud in the garden in Aeschylus' words: 'Once more thy heavy hand with ease hath ruined me.'

It was a curious holiday for me, that time in the garden— a time not of creative work, nor of any achievement, but of creative thought, so clear and so sustained within myself, that it seemed poetry born into the world no less surely than if it had been written. Poetry, not poems. To see, or to observe one thing, and at that same instant for the soul (it is too instantaneous for the mind) to give birth to its matching half, its sunny shadow. Such swift mental images I had constantly and they made me very happy. For that was why I was born, to be able to do just that and nothing else.

John Custance writes of the 'demons' whom he saw and conversed with. Now I had my demons also and I began perhaps at this time (August), perhaps a little later, to associate the ring of great men and women I had admired and loved all my life, with such; but not if one takes the word 'demon' to mean an evil spirit. Not that, indeed, but a *familiar* spirit. They had retreated from me after the fit and I had abandoned my book on Emily Brontë. They now returned. Byron, Bach, Isaac Newton, Jacob Stainer, Cassandra and the Brontë girls. I am not now writing chronologically— in the state which writing now induces in me, it is doubtful if I could. But roughly in the period between the first and second attacks, these figures appeared once more to dominate my hopes and my dreams. Such a phase, even lifelong, is common, of course. Many people are bound by such 'daemons'—to give a famous example or two: Shelley by the ancient Greeks, Blake by Milton, and Wordsworth by Milton, Vaughan by Herbert, etc. It is admiration which resurrects these dead men and women and makes them living companions. Sometimes fear or posthumous hatred can do so; but I never had a 'daemon' I feared, though several I did not like. Of all these people I experienced the most vivid, the most brilliant dreams; I saw Stainer: there was so much hair about his face and head and his manacled mad hands were covering his mouth, that all that was visible to me was his weeping eyes. I saw and talked to Byron. He was holding a fine horse by the bridle: behind him was the main gateway of some enormous mansion of which the dream showed only the left-hand pillar and a piece of the wrought-iron. He spoke to me, displaying for me the beauty of the splendid animal he held. Then in one dream, exceptional even among oddities, I went to see the Brontës. I give the account from my diary.

Last night: 'How far is it to Haworth?'

'Five miles or more. Ask at the church.'

'But it's only a mile and a half!'

'Ask at the church.'

At the church they are dancing. There are lights and the Pope is there in white. I say nothing, and pass the tower, the graves, the tall trees.

Soon I am in the Parsonage Hall: 'Anne! Emily! Charlotte!' I shout.

Anne is the first to appear. She is very small, emaciated, and she offers me a hand which I take. It shocks me it is so tiny and bony. I am very gentle with it, but even so I feel all the soft small fingers squashed in my clasp. They feel as if they have been *boiled* or simmered to a pulp with five slippery cores.

Next comes Charlotte from another door, and after her

Emily. Charlotte is dumpy, with reddish hair, a pale face and a demeanour. She has come from the parlour, Anne from the kitchen or cellar somewhere down below. Tall Emily, with dead-brown eyes and a very white face has descended from the bedroom. She looks like O—— whom I particularly dislike. And nobody speaks.

The association in this dream with the Pope and the Brontës utter lack of response to the Roman Catholic faith is amusing. These dreams and others I am careful to include, not because I am of the psychoanalytical Faith myself, but that I do believe dreams reveal the state of the brain almost as accurately as poetry. And I give two more dated about the middle of August.

'I have had two dreams of tombs, both of glass. The first dream took place by the sea where waves thick with pebbles were rolling towards a grassy shore. On that shore stood my tomb, a tiny glass thing like a gardener's cloche. Whatever was laid inside shrank to its proportions. I was not yet there, but it was fated that I should lie in it, a woman-kin, dwarfer than a herb. Edging my hand in I let it stay, but it remained large, life-sized, glassy blue and blurred.

'In the second dream the tomb was J——'s mother's. She lay in it with her face raised up in a low square tower, her body flat, her hair dressed with flowers, her face painted. The corners of the tomb were of wood. Above her head was written:

Until the Return of Life and Art.

I remembered that J——'s mother was a singer.'

It must be understood if any one gets so far in reading this MS. as this point, that although I do not really agree with any whole school of psychology as to the interpretation of dreams, I do think that, like the rainbow, they are a sign about which fables and myths (not excluding the most modern) are frequently not so much wrong as transposed. The rainbow was to be a sign of peace, a compact of wholesome weather for the human race: and from that tale has arisen the popular belief that to see a rainbow bodes fine weather. In fact, such a sight is a sign of the contrary, so far as I have observed. And this I have observed very carefully. The rainbow precedes days, and often weeks of restless storms. It betokens unhappy skies and driven trees, high winds, unseasonable influences. It is the stormy petrel of the atmosphere. Dreams, I believe, belong as much to the conscious mind as the waking actions. They can go with or against the conscience exactly as deeds do. If they go against it, however fantastically dreamed, whatever the setting, the dreamer is conscious of unease or remorse. And he will wake thinking, 'Thank God it was a dream and I didn't do it!' Nor do I think that any part of him ever wished to do that action which by waking he has escaped and by dreaming he has committed. But if he thinks out his dream thoroughly he may discover the deed he dislikes or even hates having dreamed of doing, is a fact, transposed. It is what he had dreamed of doing, in his mind, while awake, only it is in another form. It is what I call a sympathetic contradiction.

I will give an example and then finish with dreams, for I included them only that they should contribute their part to the total of my story. Thus, after the birth of my child I was afraid to go near the house of some friends who also had a baby with an infectious illness. I can honestly say that there was no fear or recoil on my own account except the most terrible personal fear of all, the fear of danger to what one loves. And therefore I had made up my mind that the only direct and simple thing to do was to avoid my friends, and if they asked the reason, to tell them the truth, curtly and without nervous excuses.

The night after I had decided this I had one of those most inexplicable of all kinds of dreams—the kind when you are leading a life you have never led in a place where you have never been, and probably as a person you are not, yet all is familiar and has apparently gone on for years. I seemed to have moved into another small cottage: and during the first months of my life in it, which appeared to pass day by day and night by night as they do in real life, my husband and I were visited every day and sometimes all day by a neighbour whom we pitied but did not like. She stayed to most meals: she was exceedingly poor, and in what she thought was return for our company and the food and drink, she began to do little things for us. I can see her as vividly as if I had really known her for a very long time, a hugely broad old woman in a very worn grey coat and skirt—very, very fat and squat, horribly obese, but with poor fat, not comfortable living. She was an intensely pathetic figure, and we endured her presence until driven to savagery by our never being alone. At last one night, I remember whispering to my husband: 'I can't endure it any more. And we can't *afford* it. Either I shall run away or I *shall tell her outright to go.*'

(I have italicized that 'tell her outright' for in that phrase lies the interpretation not of the dream but of the intention to tell my friends *outright* why I would not go to their house.)

The morning came and so did the now dreaded figure of my old fat defenceless horror. I was sitting in an arm-chair, quite silent, with a furious shut sulky look which was evidently terrifying to her for she crept about as quietly as she could, tidying away what I didn't want tidied. At last, almost in a whisper, her voice approached me, beseeching, troubled, agonized, the voice of a person who has suffered what she sees is approaching her again many times before: 'Can I get you a cup of tea, a biscuit?'

'No,' I said. 'I don't want anything!'

She went out of the room and after a moment returned with two biscuits which she sat down and ate timidly. Never in real life have I experienced such horrible sensations of atrocious pity and determined ruthlessness, for I knew as I watched her that she had not enough to eat if we cast her off. And yet, after a moment I said, with the coolest brutality, 'I don't want anything except you to go and never come back.'

She rose instantly, picked up her dirty handbag and with the dignity of those who have none, passed away forever from my knowledge. I did not call her back, but when my husband came home he found me sobbing with remorse and I begged him to find her: 'Tell her I am good natured really, but sometimes I am out of my mind.'

'Yes, I'll go, after dinner,' he said. And I could not make him see my urgency. And then I woke and the cruelty could never be undone. I was at home, in this house, this life, but I felt that she too was real—and I turned round and said to my husband I could not understand *why* I should have to have so piteous, so unnecessary a dream. It was not long before I saw the connection, and made up my mind that the mistake should not be repeated. I would not go to my friends' house, for the child's sake I could not, but I would take any pains, tell any lies, manufacture any reasons rather than 'tell them outright.'

The thought in my waking mind in the dream was the same thought, but transposed into another key. Thus, in counterpoint a theme develops, expands and contracts. Our dreams are our counterpoint: our lives set the themes. Sometimes one dreams in fine detail, as certain schools of painting reproduced Nature. Of such was this dream, for even the weather was in it. In others the detail is less even than the Impressionistic School, only a rough kind of picture or scribble of a background. Again (and these are the rarest) there are the vast dreams, when one senses and partly sees a ventured universe, huge, subtle and undefined. One dreams these last without keen sight. One dreams as though half blind.

I could, of course, analyse this dream for myself, after my beliefs, if I wished. My piteous stout 'friend' was, naturally, the family I knew. Her obesity and pertinacity were their stupidity in not guessing my motive for not visiting them. Her hunger was their human loneliness when in distress. The dream therefore was an almost complete symbol of the situation and would seem to me to illustrate my point that the dream is no more like the reality than primitive religious symbols are made to look like what they are meant to symbolize. Also that in analysing a dream, you are taking to pieces and examining conscious and not subconscious life. It is a useful and timely guide in behaviour. At this part of my book which I am now writing on the morning of September 7th, 1951, I have a strong imminent feeling of *apprehension*, of my disease rising once more, after four months of freedom, to the danger level. My physical body feels a kind of unphysical passion, and two of my images (ruling daemons), Jacob Stainer and William Wordsworth, are moving out of the circle towards me, with what message I have forgotten, only I know that as I write it will come back.

Indeed, whether we read psychoanalysis of dreams, or

of Joseph interpreting Pharaoh's, it seems clear that dreams interpret life, and not that life interprets dreams.

Prophecy being the interpretation of the Future, could there not be an interpretation of what has gone, a Prophet of the Past? Because if not they write nonsense who explain Wordsworth as Prophet, seer or mystic. His whole vision was of the beginning, and light as ancient history. He, like Vaughan, saw God behind him.

> Happy those early days, when I
> Shined in my angel infancy.

But what a curious, persistent association this is—God with light! One feels it is quite modern. Out of darkness came light, out of God came light, therefore God being the beginning, if not the end, God is darkness—a 'deep but dazzling darkness.' A more curious inversion still is the idea of darkness being devilish and evil, darkness which is the throne of the stars, and the train of the sun! There is something here which fits in with the daemon becoming the demon, a torturing spirit of evil instead of a secret and child-like and immortal Innocent of place . . . a sort of earthly angel. We humans have seized the shining outgoing, straight rod of religion, Aaron's rod, and bent it round to our own breasts until it sears and pierces our hearts. The fall of our blood we have called sacramental—and so it is, a sacrament to evil.

My demons were not wicked or frightening. They were only enclosing.

CHAPTER V

THE woman who is carrying her child, although she feels an adult and maternal responsibility for it, and a charming friendliness towards it, is not as yet so much its *mother as its twin*. At least so I felt. My child had made a choice of me. In August I was certain, for as I walked in the woods at E—— although there was no stirring in me, I discovered that I was no longer alone. And in a fit of depression I wrote a sentence which was not true of me and my child, but which belonged to the unhappy motherhood in my unfinished novel:

'This isn't a birth but a haunting': it was certainly not true of US. Of that I am sure, and therefore it is a good example of the intellectual creative understanding, which is affected by nothing except itself.

Not alone any more. Tell that to a doctor. I did not, but he told me. My body *had* made its choice and it was birth. Life, not death, unless death meant to follow. If that should be so, was it, I wondered, why I had dwelt on such a possible finality on leaving Clystowe?

To take leave of myself had become a commonplace. To create, although in another form, something from within me, was a commonplace also. Therefore, although I was over forty and had assuredly never expected mother-hood, the prospect of it was less of a shock, less of a surprise, less of a novelty, less of an untried experience than it might have been to some one much younger and in more perfect health. Triumph I did feel, inseparable from the fulfilment of the purpose for which I was a woman: but I confess that it was a lesser one than I had already had in finding a child in the womb of my brain. Humanly it may be the supreme outlet for a woman's passion—to bear a child; but artistically it is not; and I will never agree that it can lastingly influence a woman artist away from her greatest instinct. The neglect of many children by intellectual mothers may be due to this—that the brain and the womb are enemy cities, and the inhabitants of them are born to strive with one another. It came to me slowly and comfortingly that in spite of mental eccentricities, mental *underlinings* as it were of the character I was, the balance must be essentially true that my mind received the child as naturally as my body. It brought less shock of pleasure than achievement in other ways: it brought responsibility into my life, which no work of art does, being created adult, and separate, and finished when it is finished, where the child is infinite and never apart any more than the Universe is. It made art for the moment—and by art I mean mental creation—seem not unimportant but unlikely. It was much more peaceful, much more inexorable and unchangeable than anything that had ever happened to me. For whereas in art one is incessantly trying not only to excel oneself, but if one is an honest artist, to excel the possibilities one contains, in maternity one does nothing at all except what is sensible. And what a change to be sensible instead of trying to be inspired! The ease of it, the rotund relaxation, the complacency! Especially when one has experienced, I will not say madness, but a certain similarity, when one is the orphan of reason, if not its lost ground.

But I forget; I was not yet the orphan of reason, that came later. At this stage I was still hoping that Professor T——'s remark that I might never have another fit if I followed the treatment might be the truth. And therefore, remembering his words about my epilepsy being caused *in all likelihood* by a small scar on the brain, comparatively comfortable about the unborn child. However, I was not to escape without plunging far deeper into the darkness of epilepsy than that.

One morning in our cottage I got up fairly early out of bed and went downstairs to make tea. I carried the tray upstairs, put it down by the bed and the next moment it seemed heard my husband saying to me as my head lay on the pillow: 'How do you feel, dearie?'

Astonished, I answered drowsily that I felt very well, why? 'Because you have just had another attack,' he said. With those words an amazement entered into me which has never left me. Ever since I have been incredulous of all things firm and material. The light has held patches of invisible blackness, Time has become as rotten as worm-eaten wood, the earth under me is full of trap-doors and the sense of being, which is life and all that surrounds and creates it, a thing taken and given irresponsibly and without warning as children snatch at a toy. Sight, hearing, touch, consciousness, torn from one like a nest from a bird!

Of course it was only slowly I realized the truth as my eyes discovered a blood-stained pillow-case, my senses a tongue bitten through at the edge, for it seemed he had had as little warning as myself. It had been a swift performance. One kick, he said, as I lay down, and he cried, 'What are you doing?' and turned and saw. It had lasted twenty minutes. He had changed the pillow-case under my head. Twenty minutes! and less than a blink to me, for this time, as I had been lying in bed and was not hurt apart from my tongue, I felt no illness afterwards. In fact the tea was still hot and we drank it quite as usual. This was my second major or total attack of epilepsy. It was strange, I thought, how ahead almost of the instantaneous, one disappears into epileptic oblivion, and how slowly and wanderingly one leaves it, roaming, and grasping at one's familiar surroundings like a person hauling himself through a thick dark wood by holding on to the extended branches of the trees.

I did not find these total fits (of which I had only two) anything like so horrible as those decreased, or slowed down by the drugs as the rest were to be. In the complete instantaneous loss of consciousness, oblivion is ahead of sensation as I have said. In the case of the decreased and dwindling attack which follows the treatment by drugs, and leads finally often to freedom from the disease, the reverse is the order, and sensation is ahead of oblivion by several seconds which seem themselves whole universes of a terribly helpless, *silly* and yet 'knowing' existence. I use those words 'silly' and 'knowing' in their combined sense of the word 'cunning'. For hideous as it seems, for some seconds, the brain of the sufferer appears to think it can elude the inevitable darkness by a sort of cunning—a sort of crude shiftiness. The final feeling in a decreased fit, before unconsciousness supervenes is, as it were, a giggling irresponsibility. It is the most appalling, the most horrifying experience I have passed through, those final stages of consciousness. However, I have not yet come to that; and will do so later. My recovery from the second major fit was very quick. I had had no blows; and within a few minutes after becoming conscious and hearing his voice we were sitting up drinking the tea which was still hot.

But, as I have said, my security was gone. From then onward I never felt sure when I might be doing something normal one moment, and the next hear some one saying:

'How do you feel?' Things no longer flowed, no longer joined. It was as if one were able to see dry patches of ground suddenly in the course of a rolling river. Every one knows what electricity cuts are or a fuse from lightning when every light goes out. Imagine that darkness, and yourself going with the light, to reappear when it comes on again, *but doing something totally different*.

There was also the dismal medical aspect. I do not seem to have written anything in my diary except this significant note:

'Of course I realize that two fits are more than twice as serious as one.'

And then on August the 20th.

'I wish I hadn't this poor mole of a child in me, whose rising presence in the cottage is less than the disease. There is then a real flaw. There will be other attacks. What to *do*? M—— said as soon as he had said to me, "You've had another attack," I said emphatically, "The child mustn't be born," and groaned. I don't remember that—I can't have been fully conscious; but I was right, oh I was right!'

I went to the Maternity Hospital, to the clinic. The doctor didn't even look at me.

'You will have your baby here!' he shouted from behind some curtains.

'But I am an epileptic!' (!!)

'All the more reason to have it here and not at home.'

What I had meant was, ought I to have it? He did not come out, so I dressed and came away. And Dr. Y—— had made a special appointment for me to see him! Well, if I must have it I need not live, nor when it comes to the struggle, help it into the world.

People who could help me have written to me and asked me why not have it quietly removed and I have replied that since the second fit that is my wish and that if they knew of any one who would do it, please help me. There, that's enough, it's making me mad without writing as well as thinking endlessly about it. Epilepsy and pregnancy. The shock of waking every morning to such a grim problem of life.

And characteristically, this footnote:

'But perhaps I shan't live long. I could die very lazily.'

But no normal pregnant woman can think of the extinction of her child, her mysterious twin, without anguish. My horror of the twist in my brain, of its possible inheritance by my baby, may have made it *seem* that I was anxious not to bear it. But it was not so, truly, and never can I forget Dr. Y——'s kindness, his encouragement and firmness. It was needed, I do not know if he saw how desperately, for neither can I forget the month of indecision which followed, when roaming and incessantly arguing within myself, the chances of which I knew nothing one way or the other, I learned the stormy countryside by another sense than the heart or the mind. One 'walk' indeed is indelible—I had rushed out of the cottage alone, in a solitude such as only the driven can remember having experienced—such a solitude as I have heard in the screams of violins, seen in tumbled and tossed skies blackened by rain with leaping branches and shapes of lightning, or followed, stricken by, rather than listening to, the frightful piano sonatas of Beethoven, that terrible music which broke music and which (I think) finished it. Indeed, as I rushed through the valleys, woods and fields, all cold, wet, hollow-smelling and prematurely rotting from the wet summer, it was of the C Minor Sonata I thought. Where was my Earth? It was buried, like Beethoven's peace, in the screams of his deafness, the frenzies that tore away his divine themes and twisted them into enormous chords or colossal rushes up and down the keyboard. How I found my way I do not know, for I did not see it, nor really remember it. It was solved for me as it happened, like the C Minor, by the art learned and discovered before the disease which thwarted those descending half tones and maligned those most serene melodies. No 'sane' mind could have produced such music: no 'sane' mind could have seen the earth as I saw it that day—John Clare's earth and Jacob Stainer's and Heathcliff's. But no 'sane' mind has ever made or done anything, be the vision in art or wood or memory.

If I had been younger I might either have completed my insanity then, or killed myself almost carelessly, in my stride. But as the adagio breaks softly and slowly into the Sonata to lull it, and then to awaken it to the exquisite flying joy of the rondo, my years of gazing familiarly at this earth, which is to be my most beautiful grave, slowed and saved me. First I saw one recognizable thing and then another as though recovering from a fit, which is, however it may be without a vision, a vision in itself . . .

I say 'saved' and I have said before 'rescued.' It is not the right word. The sight of lovable and recognizable earth saved me no more than it saves the life of an air pilot who is not killed by a fall against it. Neither is it chance. A return. That is all.

I am aware that all along I have been using the wrong terms, the wrong words. Perhaps the right ones exist, perhaps not. I am now too tired for the Search, the Choice. I do not like to use such educated, such particular comparisons as the one I have made with the C Minor Sonata. Not every one has heard and fewer *know* the Sonata, but every one has been at one time desperate and short of any solution to existence, every one has experienced a heart that seems to swim in refusal, division and grief like a small bubble in a great storm. Yet I *did* think of the Sonata, and of Beethoven's wonderful and frightful music at that time. It is part of what we lose when we grow up, that in feeling our own tempests we think of others; that in suffering we suffer not simply and centredly but many of us very much too diffusely: in short, that as we grow older all that we see and feel is as much what others have seen and felt as our own. The earth becomes more and more like a history book and less and less like a wonder; that it should be so is inevitable because of our own accumulating memories alone.

I felt this now. Before me was a gate, a dark naked hill. Behind lay the woods, sodden and wrecked, sour-smelling, hollow, with their greeny-yellow leaves clashing. In the beech trees hung the first striplings of autumn, gold and sodden. Near to me were blackberry bushes in flower and fruit—the pink petals and the white. Not only the lead of a raindrop, the weight of a breeze, hung on those well-known flowers, dropping them to the grass, but how many seasons of my own sight of them! How many years of mine, how many memories, associations, selves, were they showing to me? I was recalled to *myself* by twenty other selves dependent upon the sloes among the spiny twigs, and the column of gnats rising and falling like steam against some dark tree trunks and leaves. And I returned home quite quietly, without knowing what I must do, but nevertheless still capable of doing something.

In the end it was decided that the best thing was to ask Dr. H——, medical authority in charge at the St. Ides epileptic colony, for his advice, and my husband and I went very soon after to my sister's once more.

The day before we went we were gardening when Dr. Y—— came out from Cheltenham. He had always maintained that as far as the child was concerned, all would be well, though he thought it quite wise to consult Dr. H—— who happened to be a very old friend of his.

I can see Dr. Y—— now, standing in the cottage garden, an open book in his hand, his finger on the page keeping the wind down, reading over his glasses a passage from *Nervous Diseases* by the Professor of Neurology at London University, which he said was the last and most up-to-date work on epilepsy. This paragraph declared in effect that the liberty of epileptic people in the matter of sex, marriage and childbirth, had always been unwarrantably constricted, and that there was in reality only the very slightest danger of its being hereditary.

'So there you are!' cried he, with a piercing look, and drove off in triumph.

We had such an admiration for Dr. Y—— that it was a most unhappy surprise to me to find that Dr. H—— did not agree with this view. He had had twenty-five years of practical experience among epileptics. He asked me a lot of questions about the two fits I had had which I answered from the description of the last my husband had given me. He looked at my tongue which was green and swollen still where it had been bitten. Finally, 'Hum,' said he, 'I don't wonder you're worried. The best thing in my opinion for you to do is to follow Dr. Y——'s advice and ask him to get Professor T—— to see you at once. At once. For if they are going to operate it must be soon.

'It is a horrible thing,' he said as he walked with my sister and me to the door, and then with a glittering look of pure concentration, 'but how interesting!'

I thought so and think so still.

'Dr. H—— and Dr. Y—— are two kind, good, brave men,' I wrote in my diary. 'Dr. H—— says we can only go by what Professor T—— says.'

Professor T—— agreed with Dr. Y——. He saw me on September 29th when I was four months gone with child. It was a quiet warm day, and the Professor spoke to me in a soft, haughty voice. Before my inward eyes, this man seemed to spread the authoritative, the peacock, wings of an archangel. The child was to live. It was to be true. It was mine and I was to keep it. As he told me I wasn't suffering from the hereditary type of epilepsy and so could not pass it on, two tears rose to my eyes and slowly spilled. One it seemed was mine, and one the child's. They were all I had to say to him, to truth and to God.

CHAPTER VI

The Affirmative

The Professor's face did not change as he saw our tears. Neither did his voice move up or down from its usual proud and soft note as he continued:

'Epilepsy is so common a trouble that there is, of course, always a chance that any woman may have an epileptic child. But you no more than any other. Do you know, have you any idea how many epileptic people there are walking about, taking part in public life? I am sure you have not. In Switzerland, for instance, where a census of them was taken the percentage was as high as one in a hundred. And if that was admitted you may be sure that in truth it was more than twice as high.'

And he continued: 'In every European country where the disease has been carefully notified and studied they have entirely failed to prove that it is hereditary. There is only one kind that we regard as dangerous in such a way and that is where it is accompanied by mental defectiveness.'

He paused and for the first time showed me his irradiating smile.

'That is obviously not your type,' said Professor T——. 'Go home then, live as you have always lived, work your brain for that is good for it, and ask Dr. Y—— to let me know when the child is born. I shall want to see it, you know, for your sake. We will make an encephalogram so that you won't worry. And now you must go.'

I walked out into the sunlight where my friend was

waiting for me and we ran downhill. That day I bought the first clothes for my baby.

I must now go back three or four months and incidentally return to the question which I have not yet been able to ask Professor T——, namely, whether there can be a connection between epilepsy and a spiritual hunger? Can it, in fact, be a religious disease which attacks the physical being, such as many diseases of mental origin, as Proust observes, undoubtedly do. As there is a relationship between the severer digestive troubles and stress and strain, worry and hurry, can there be a lack of defined faith in fits? *Can* the loving and grateful heart live without love and gratitude? Can the worshipful exist without worship, the believer without God? Only defectively it would seem.

The epileptic is bound to be reminded that his roots are in darkness far more often and more acutely than the ordinary person. Also he is compelled, like the life of nature, to return and dwell in the root whereas the ordinary person is not attached to any under existence except his own individual one of the mind. The epileptic seems to be in a constant communion, dumb so far as memory is concerned, with a *general* and dark source of being. One might put it that an ordinary person's is animal life, an epileptic's plant life. The animal person (i.e. the normal) having no certain source of dismay in himself, turns to artificial and collective forms of it, insists upon 'facing up to things' which he has himself created, and accuses those who do not wish to probe, read, write and talk about these things, of 'escapism.' The plant person (i.e. one who is afflicted with a mental, physical or nervous disease) has more of a tendency to be an 'escapist' or 'wishful thinker,' etc., and to search for:

'Whatsoever things are true, whatsoever things are just,

whatsoever things are pure, whatsoever things are lovely, whatsoever things are of good report, and if there be any virtue and if there be any praise' to 'think on these things.'

So that an epileptic, if he is not born religious, is likely to become so out of his unconscious and profound excursions into infinity. He must find God, or the Source which arbitrarily and often absorbs himself. The healer of Death, the world's greatest and most famous physician, the greatest doctor to mental maladies ever recorded, said to the sufferer of a nervous disease, on sight, 'Son, thy sins be forgiven thee.' And in easing the spiritual strain, fulfilled the physical cure. To grant a wish is to cure a pain. Money buys evil but not good, and the world, the temple, is become a den of thieves.

Professor T—— once said to me that having satisfied himself of a patient's brain being physically sound, he turned away and left the way open to the priest. Professor T—— believes in religion. He told me so. I too believe in religion but for me there could be no priest. I myself must find God. I believe also that any one who searches for truth for himself will end by finding it even if it is only a tiny morsel, and that that tiny morsel will be a part of the undiscoverable whole which is God the creator and God the lover and God the inspirer. To reach a point where one can find God the creator is very much easier than to go infinitely beyond and discover God's love. For every person is really not searching for a God who has created a universe but one who has created him himself, individually, his character, his body, his necessities and to whom this God will give out of the whole, one special piece of pure, precious reciprocal love.

I found the God of Creation when I was writing *Autobiography*, at the end of it. The God of Love I shall probably never find, for search as I will I see no signs of protective pleasure, or tenderness or even *observation* extended towards what has been created by what has created it.

I say, probably never. But the search goes on, and now I could not write as I did in *Autobiography:* 'There is a God, but to Him we can give only the same heart that we give to humanity.'

Nothing, as I feel it now (September 1950), could be more untrue. We cannot give the same heart to humanity that we would to God, for humanity neither needs nor demands such a love. God is at your hand, and yet to carry to him your heart you must go outside the world.

It seems to me that the love of humanity is a useful and necessary affection. We all need it: it is only a natural thing, a comradeship for life. And no one should make more of it than a daily errand. As a Creed, as a Passion it is an insipid one: as Politics it is a busybody's business and not a genuine one. Without decrying humanitarianism, it is not, except for a few of us, difficult to attain, nor should it be, for is not our neighbour, to all balanced people, oneself? compelled to die and to suffer pain before death?

Love thy neighbour does not include love thy God, and it will not take the place of spiritual development. It is easy to conceive of most wicked, most selfish men being in constant communication with God, and being beloved by Him, for God is a matter of communion and development and inspiration and not of virtue. Those who suffer spiritually, who have felt the injustice of eternity and their own weakness, might be dear to God in a way that the most placid, busy humanitarian could never be. The ancients believed this: it is symbolized by the particular destiny divinely reserved for such cruel and cunning men as Joseph, Cain, etc., characters whom most of us despise as we read of their successfulness. It would seem that to the divine power, great evil is as open a channel as great goodness. Once we have grasped the love of God as a thing within, a thing separate, uninfluenced by the rest of the character, much old and wise symbolism becomes clearer. It explains the figure of David, the radiant king, the great poet and sinner, and in some measure his son Solomon. It explains God's love for the rebellious Job. The God I would find is the creator of the Muse or the Daemon in men and women: the maker of the free, the wild, the rebellious, the beautiful and the savagely innocent. He is Nature in Earth, and nature in us. God the friend, God the friend of humanity left when Adam lost Paradise. Instead of the comrade who walked and talked in the garden at evening, there was the Creator, the Holy One everywhere traceable, yet closed:

'In some one corner of a feeble heart.' One may, if one wishes, at times observe his thoughts, and hear, in such as Bach and Beethoven, the fragments of his voice.

To imagine that one conceives of the maker of the universe, by being a moral or a kind person, however gentle, however constant, is as strange as for one to roll in the surf and the froth and to think one has felt the ocean's depth: or to see the light of a star and think one has kissed its burning face. Surely, to give one love to humanity and *another* to God is the true meaning of render unto Caesar?

I have spent so many laboured words on this because when I first began to take the drugs prescribed for epilepsy I had an experience which, however poorly I managed to express it in words, I think my life is unlikely now to alter and although there remained before me much strain, horror and mental distress, it is to that day when words and belief met and fused quite suddenly, I believe I owe the improvement in my disease more distinctly perhaps than to physical treatment. But belief and faith are not one and the same; and I honestly confess that I would not dare to rely for my present peace on that confession and affirmation alone.

When Professor T—— and Dr. Y—— first began to prescribe for me I was nervous of being alone in the cottage. No one of my family was free to stay with me and it was impossible for my husband to interrupt his course at St. Paul's College. Some one, however, came and I remember one day Dr. Y—— saying:

'Have you found an old cow to stay with you?'

'No, a man is coming.'

'A *bull*, eh?' and the doctor laughed.

The *bull* was a tall, slender young man, a very, very old friend of mine whom I had known since he was a boy. A descendant of Shelley, a poet himself, who had been in the R.A.M.C., no one could have been more apt. He left his own cottage in Herefordshire where he lived alone and wrote, and came and stayed with me. My introduction to the drugs proved absolutely successful, I had no fits and B—— and I lived extremely amicably, squabbling over poetry, reading, the cooking and everything except our passion for village and field life. B—— however found me too sociable, for I knew not only my generous neighbours up the road who had helped me when I had had the midnight attack, but the Postmistress and the friend who kept the tiny shop. B—— declared that in *his* more perfect retirement he knew nobody—and that there was nobody to know. Also that his weeds were much larger than ours.

This I found to be quite true. For during one week we

returned to B——'s cottage in order that he might continue
to dig up a few. And although six feet high B—— disappeared among the nettles and docks when gardening,
which he did in a very strange and oriental manner that
must have caused great mystification in Herefordshire.
He dug in circles, beginning round his feet and reappearing
hours later with a desperate expression and a fearful appetite.
For he explained of his austere existence: 'I love cooking,
but I don't like what I cook.' This had led to a more or
less natural separation between his appetite and what he
provided for it. As he had been living alone for some
time, he had a lot of time to make up.

Cooking was all I ever did in B——'s cottage. We
neither dusted nor swept. It was in many ways a nicer
cottage than ours. It was slightly larger and full of cupboards—so full that one could never find anything as B——
hated method more than neighbours. The garden was full
of beautiful roses which toiled over the roofs of out-
buildings; and a narrow red stream trickled under alders
at the back of the garden—it was wonderful to see the deep
red earth again, and the hills, it was wonderful and hateful. For the only abiding and bitter resentment I have felt
against my life was there being no place for me in that
home country I had moulded out of my heart. Nothing
has been really visible to my inner eyes since I left it—and
I was there for a week! at midsummer. I wrote in my diary:

'It's a little white cottage, quiet in a perpetual hush.
After the last few weeks, what silence! For what a chatter
the advent of a disease causes. Almost it makes *parties*. But
not here among the bracken and the foxgloves. Murmur,
murmur go the wild bees in the garden among the high
weeds. The dew and the rain falls, the summer fire sighs
in the evening, the brook runs downhill. It's like living in

a leaf, in a flower, in a scent, so near are the banks of the little valley, so close the sleepy leaves.'

It was midsummer and the cuckoo was retreating. It was that lovely time when the rain polishes the green corn, when the hedgerows glitter with each wild strawberry leaf and flower, and my own hills shone with intense blue lustre. Across a line of that blue, only just on the other side, I had lived and written *Autobiography*. There were my thoughts and my life impressed, and here stood I on the other side of them as isolated as I felt.

I was telling this to myself one long day in the lane when B—— had gone on the bus to Abergavenny to get food. It was a glad yet bitter feeling I had looking at the elms on their tall stalk trunks with the heavy high-hung foliage that is somehow like dark summer shadows on grass reared upright—a near, yet distant emotion. They seemed, those elms and those hills, and those lanes as deep as overgrown moats of ancient fortresses, friends absent, yet present in remembrance, never to be encountered again because the phase of life to which they belong is irrecoverably past. And there came into my mind then Albert Schweitzer's discovery of 'a wonderful serene longing for death,' in Bach's music. My longing had been called debased and morbid. And I asked myself when did I, like a dying heroine in a nineteenth-century romance, 'give up hope'? When did I cease to believe I should have an old age in which to see the glory of earth and life die away like light fading in light? When did I cease to want it? What faith, or belief was mine? Was it still that I should survive in Nature, but not in any other way?

I was looking over the valleys towards my old country when these questions seemed to answer themselves spontaneously in two lines. Those two lines of words embodied my mind and heart as no poems I had ever written had done, and a sort of spiritual and literary and physical finality took place then in me. Something unalterable had happened and declared itself. Hurrying downhill to B——'s cottage I found pencil and paper, and on my knees, on the floor of my bedroom with the sweet smell of the rain coming in through the window I finished the sonnet. There were to be several revisions of the words but none of the thought. This is the final version achieved:

The Education

Knowledge in me is like a peasant nun
whose learning stopped at God and God alone;
all growth is God is all that I have known,
stops at this education, moon and sun,

the weedy world, light ended and begun,
and Night and Fear, and Death and every tone
the pleasures sang. But now has been upthrown
the first earth for my grave, and my days run
to darkness underneath, what is the last
and final version chosen by thy breath
oh all-felt God, whose presence in the past
was common touch like grass and daily bread?
It is to find thee sick, to see thee dead
though I am dead and thou remaineth Death.

That sonnet contains indeed all that I am capable of believing. I may develop further but I do not think it likely. It is as a man's vocation which he has confessed and has cast into the form of his vows. Once written, I did not ask those questions again. The sonnet brought an answer which was no answer except that the Creator is divine because He lives if only as Death after we die and He is always life and death though our consciousness of His being so is no longer in existence.

It brought no comfort and no illumination in the illness which followed, when the disease, slowed by the drugs, became so terrifying, not only because of its avowal, but because the brain when attacked by a fit is incapable of 'thinking' but only of certain reactions which I shall now try to describe. It was like Professor T—— when he said to me at our first interview, 'There is no cure. We never speak of a cure,' better said, because possibly modifiable.

PART THREE

Gemini

There is a star that waits for me;
(where my place is my light will be)

so dark we two have been apart!
as traveller's home and traveller's heart.

For when to Earth my heart was driven
each pledged to each what gifts were given

being certain neither it nor I
was shaped by shape of wind to die:

it holds my voice in it secure
and I, in me, its light immure:

for that no one has heard me here
where mists tread down the fields of fear,

or heard me sing; or seen its light
beyond the outmost glasses's might.

But ah, my twin, the change is due
the pledge is kept, the pang is through.

Darkness goodnight! in its own speech
(Goodnight is dark) I'll cry and reach

to learn by presence that which some
call the Eternity to come

and I call Everlasting Time,
uninterruptedly to shine

and hover in us both and sing
with unity in everything.

CHAPTER I

THAT poem, written in October 1951, was addressed both to my child and to death, separately, or together.

'When mists tread down the fields of fear.' Winter in E—— at nearly a thousand feet up, was beginning. Cloud-fogs blew along the plateau where the village rested—different from valley fogs because they were as full of movement as valley fog is of stillness. They were like sheep—a flock of fogs that rolled past the windows of the cottage and could be seen winding across field and wood.

The berries fell, the bracken faded. From the ricks nearby mice stole into our cupboards. Our cat caught them but as she was full and didn't seem to know what to do with them, we rescued them.

At dinner one day, M—— said, 'Oh I forgot. I've got a mouse in my pocket,' and he took it out and held it in his hand: 'A very brave mouse,' he observed watching it brush its whiskers into order—a rather *flat* grey field-mouse with eyes like pin-holes. He said it was having a rest cure. Certainly it seemed brisk, but for safety's sake, as he had to go out, I put it in my pocket. As I was working later on I felt something at the back of my neck. The mouse, forgotten again, had come out and ran up and down my arm. I let it go in the garden, and it went, but only very gradually and rather grudgingly.

On October 24th I fancied I had had one of my old very slight attacks of dizziness; and this encouraged me to believe that the worst was past and I was returning to what was normal for me. It made me very carefree.

But on October 31st, just as I was going to eat my lunch, having done a whole morning's washing, I was shown abruptly that there was no truth yet in believing myself better.

The food was on the table, the oil-stove lit. I picked up the coffee percolator to fill it. Just as I reached the sink and was standing in the doorway, I found I could not move, could not remember what I wanted to do. It seemed a long time that I stood there (actually perhaps a few seconds) saying to myself, 'This is nothing. It will be all right in a moment and I shall remember *all the rest*.' Then I felt my head beginning to jerk backwards and my face to grimace. Then the percolator fell from my hand into the sink. But still some dogged part of me kept saying, 'All this is really controllable.' I was still conscious and felt violent gestures and spasms were shooting all over me, even till I felt my knees give and I fell down on the concrete floor. As I went, it shot through me, the astonishment: 'As bad as this then?'

The next thing I remember was the B——s' kitchen and Betty B——, God bless her, giving me tea and talking to me in the tone mothers use to little children coming out of nightmares. Rosie was by me, sitting at my feet. I asked the time. They said it was two o'clock. Half an hour had *gone*. I had not the slightest recollection of picking myself up or walking 100 yards up the road or going into their kitchen. Nor for an hour or two, of what had happened before I fell. This came back to me by degrees as I waited with them until M—— should be home from College; but the return to action never. It is always so—the last few seconds are preternaturally distinct—the last sight always particularly remembered, as if the warning symptoms of a fit were an emotion by which all things are charged with extra reality and significance: but the coming round is an obscurity that never lifts.

Major B—— went back to the cottage and found my spectacles broken on the concrete floor. I had evidently trodden on them as I got up. I had cut my eyebrow, bruised my cheek, bruised my hand, my shoulder and my knee; and yet for anything I had felt in crashing down on that concrete floor, it might have been a feather-bed.

The B——s had a tea-party in the next room to where I was sitting waiting and gazing out on a lovely blooming sunny afternoon. I did not feel safe enough to leave them because I always dreaded another fit coming on top of the one just passed; yet I wondered how many people could have behaved as they did, cheerfully, naturally, asking me to join them, and as I grew more firm, talking to me through the doorway.

Yet I was in a way uncomforted, for I had on me that abrupt shadow of difference which falls from time to time on unhappy persons. And all the old dreadful questions came back—where had I *been*, *what* had I been. What had I said, what had I looked like, as I walked in, I asked them. 'You said you had had another fit, that's all, and we made you sit down,' they answered, 'don't you remember that? You seemed to know exactly what you were doing, and you sat down as if you'd just dropped in. Only you weren't walking very steadily.'

After this I ceased to assure myself that I had come to some sort of terms with my pursuer: and the horror which I had *refused* to admit, I had to confess to myself. If the drugs could do no more than prolong consciousness into the fit, then I would rather fall as I did at first, knowing nothing.

But Dr. Y—— came out the next day and said it was

impossible to tell how many fits I might have if I did not take the drugs. Also that in his opinion there was a decided weakening in their severity. And so I continued to take them. Six weeks later I had another. I was still strong and very well. I was never afraid out of doors, for the earth was softer than the cottage floors, and I was now quite certain I should come home. Deep in my mind was a trust of the B——s that no brain tempest could overset apparently—something unreachable, something beyond the brain's power to alter—an instinct as sure perhaps as a spirit's for the place or the person it haunts. To this I committed myself; and rightly, for no harm came of it. I suffered no dangerous injury, and my child suffered none. This time I fell down in the sitting-room doorway with the coal bucket in my hand, just as I was going to make up the fire. Just as with the last one there was that dramatic moment of standstill, as though the very blood had stopped in the veins, with a shock to all the system. A stampede of cattle arrested by a fire might send such a shock through the ground. I remember I could think, for my reaction was to tell myself *in words*, 'Get out of this doorway. There isn't room to fall.'

I thought I did. I thought I backed out into the narrow passage. The next moment it seemed I was walking up the lane in the rolling mist and drizzle, sobbing dementedly—wailing like the dispossessed—and that a man had his arm round my waist and was looking into my face. I can recollect lifting my eyes to his face. It was that of a young man from the village with whom I had had some bitter words over my dog. We had never spoken since. A look of purest compassion had transformed the face which used always to pass so dourly; and it was with the greatest gentleness he took me back into the cottage and put me into a chair while he went to fetch Major B———. I suppose they were gone about ten minutes; and in that time my strange, unusual and terrible weeping did not cease, for I could hear it. It had never happened before; but it has done ever since, every time I have an attack.

I sat there shattered, yet trying to tell myself why I was crying and sobbing with such utter grief. I told myself it was shock: I told myself it was because I had allowed myself once more to hope it was over. But I was certain within myself it was neither. It was certainly grief, the most profound, the most mysterious, but the cause was forgotten—was lost in those minutes of obliteration. So one will weep for awful loss, and the impetus of the emotion will go on even while in exhaustion the meaning of the tears that are still falling is forgotten. But I felt in some obscure way that my soul had been somewhere or seen some one who was Peace and completion, and that it had left that presence to come back into me.

In a few moments Major B——— returned. He made up the fire and came to me saying, 'Come out of this room, Margiad. Come and sit down. I have made some tea. Come and sit by the fire. It's awfully cold.'

With him I revived and gradually the dreadful inexplicable sorrow faded away and we sat talking. Major B——— told me how the young man had seen me come out of the cottage with Rosie and had stopped me because, he said, I was all over the road, and had anything come round the bend both my dog and myself must have been killed. I had not moved out of the sitting-room doorway, he said, as there on the stone step down to the room lay all the evidence—the coal bucket upside down, my glasses, unbroken this time, and the table and chair just inside, pushed over. As soon as I could walk and was myself, he

149

took me home with him until his wife returned, or my husband got back from College.

The fits were gradually getting closer upon one another, but at this period they came only in cycles of about six to eight weeks. I said to Mrs. B—— the next day that now we should have a bit of peace for a while; but I had another within eight days. I had been washing again: it was a wet cold day, and the very small cottage was crowded with clothes drying on horses. I took Rosie for our afternoon stroll in the wood and gathered some kindling. Coming in wet through, I suddenly felt ill and tired and though I knew I ought to sit down and have a meal it was impossible to find room to do so before clearing the clothes horses away and getting it. All this I did very slowly and weakly, feeling worse every moment; but at last the fire was blazing behind the guard, Rosie and I were dry, and the tea was on the table. I had just sat down when again the shock came—I half rose in the chair, in the panic that precedes the fit—that panic which makes one do something, though it is seldom anything useful or wise—and then once more I was sipping hot tea *in the other room* with Mrs. B—— sitting on the other side of the fire. It seemed quite natural and not at all as though anything had happened because my brain was still partly numb and I had forgotten everything. Indeed, I saw her smile a little as I said: 'Oh Betty, how can I thank you! If you hadn't come in I really think I should have collapsed.'

Later she remarked, 'Don't you remember me asking you if you could get up? Because you did get up at once and I put your arm over my shoulder and got you in here. You were lying on the floor in the kitchen. I knocked and couldn't get any answer, so as Rosie barked and she is never left alone, I came in. You were lying with your head in the cupboard just moving one arm. You were coming round, so I waited. And now, dear, I really don't think you should live alone all day any more.'

I told her Dr. Y—— had said the same thing directly he had heard I had been wandering in the lane; but that it was hard to find anybody even if we could afford one and we had thought there was time to search.

We did find some one, and some one who was not afraid, for her mother had been an epileptic, attacked in middle-age suddenly, just as I had been. She was such a beautiful young girl, with so excellent an intellect (I *mean* intellect and not intelligence), so courageous, and so wise on all natural life, that she might have been Wordsworth's lost Lucy. In natural science, this young girl, trained only by her own sight, and never away from her own native village, was a genius. Many strolls we took finding unusual berries and plants, fossils and mosses, wintry stories of the ancient Cotswold Hills. Her mind, her observations, were infinitely superior to mine, but she had not written or could not write what she knew. My benefactor and friend to whom I have dedicated this book sent me about now a present of money for the baby. As it was for the baby's safety, I spent it on paying this young and brave companion for the work she did for me. I had no fits all the time she was with me, and she was with me until the day my child was born—her hands helped me into the ambulance, and her hands cleaned the cottage for my husband while I was in the hospital, until we moved. She was a reserved, rather than a shy companion, and like a native of her woods, has never visited me since, as though for her as for me, there lies no temptation to linger for one afternoon even in cities. I missed her very much and for almost as long a time as I missed the places we used to go to, in the snow, under the spruce and larch and fir trees in the silent white woods. But like their shadow she could not leave them.

The gift from my own and my child's benefactor arrived exactly when it was so badly needed, and when an editor friend of many years had prayed to Saint George to take me and my baby into his keeping. Having no faith, having found no loving God, I could not ask for us myself: but I thought that the great Saint, the only one whom God had even called 'his son' had love to give to believers and perhaps to those who could only go such a short way towards the Creator as myself. And so I asked my friend to ask for me. And he did so. And Saint George protected us and my child was born safely, after that long hard winter of blows, snow, ice and fog, when the sheen of the ice had lain for six weeks on the roads and lanes, like a linen damask forced into pattern by our feet and the tractor wheels—a surface on which few could stand, but I had walked every day, carrying my child within me and the arms of a faith I could not find.

There is only one more fit I wish to describe briefly before I try to analyse the inner meanings, the emotions and the mystery, aroused in those who undergo these visitations. It happened in the Maternity Hospital, eight days after my baby was born. I was lying still in the evening after the visitors had gone, when the voiceless call came that commanded me as always to do that which it did not tell me; and as usual I substituted action, and rose up in my bed. Then I must have fallen back. The next moment it seems I woke in sorrow. I was alone. I could not remember who or where I was: but messages trying to inform me kept flashing to me and then fading again leaving blanks in my mind that were like the air under flight. I turned over and saw a screen around me. Also there was profound silence in the small ward. I stared at the screen which gradually told me of my world, and then rolling back to the wall, sobbed out to my fellow patients to ask the nurse to come. When she did, I said to her (for I had forgotten the previous sensations as always), 'I'm sure I've had a fit because of the blanks in me.' She did not say anything and when I next looked she was gone. But on the locker lay a table-spoon carefully bound round with a bandage. My mind, swiftly recovering its detective power, said, 'That's what they put between your teeth,' and the preliminaries came back to me. The kind of panic which had sent me only half consciously to look for my neighbour Mrs. B——— now burst over me—that panic which her face, her voice, her presence always averted. Now there was nothing. I made the other women call the nurse, I made her ring up my husband. 'Poor man,' I heard her say, and when she returned it was not unkindly but in rather a satisfied manner she told me she had not been able to get through to him. But by that time the confusion and the terror were over because my fellow patients had very sensibly told me about the whole thing. No, I had not upset them. No, there was not much noise. 'Only just enough to let us know you weren't well. So we rang the bell.' No, it was not very long, about a quarter of an hour, and how foolish it was not to *tell* me, they added. The next day I was perfectly well, but I was never again able to feed my child.

CHAPTER II

THERE is a phrase of a dream in *Autobiography* which describes the preliminary warning of an approaching epileptic attack although it was written merely of a nightmare: 'the heart stood to meet its enemy.' After this desperate stand comes a fluttering tremulousness of body and mind. The intensity varies; but it is physically like a breeze or a gale entering one and agitating all one's being. The old idea of demoniac possession, I am sure, arose not from the onlookers of sufferers in fits but from the sufferers themselves. Because in the violent attacks one feels as though the body has been entered by a terrific alien power; and that that power is trying, after entrance, to push its way out again. It is not unlike labour, but not so intelligent. If the consciousness is prolonged until the fall, as mine has often been, the flesh with its limbs and its orderly muscles seems actually to be entangled—the body is on the point of being blown aside as if it were what mystics have called it, a curtain: or as Blake said, a shady grove.

To describe this, however vividly one may attempt it, is not to arrive at more than sensation. A terrific sensation, it is true, and one that is inaudible to the part of the brain which is still working, so *unlike life* is it. Possibly (I do not know) there *is* no part of the brain which is still working. The surprise may be registered by the mind, which my fits have made me believe, is separate from the brain. It would seem to me that the mind is a soft surface which receives the impression of thought and sensation from the brain and is therefore always slightly *behind* in recording

154

what is actually being done at the moment by the brain. It travels, like sound, behind the jet aeroplane. Therein lies the danger; for the mind is still unbelieving of danger while the brain is losing, or has lost, control of the body. The mind reassures—its very incredulity is a delay of seconds which may mean the difference between safety and an accident.

Many people, of course, get fuller intimation of an approaching fit, and longer time in which to act. Again I only write of myself. I cannot act. That sight, hearing, memory, *personality* in fact, are intact almost to the last I have proved, but *speech* and *action* are both taken away. The power of speaking is wiped from the lips—the power of motion—or reasonable motion—is stolen. One hears people ask, 'What is the matter?' One cannot answer, although one seems to know. One's eyes are nailed on an object or a face. This rigid attitude in which one seems to be listening to a call important beyond all human matters— there is of course no voice, but such is the effect, as if the last trump had blown—dissolves into a kind of hideous hovering. One turns round or away from helpers, if they are present, if not, from the presence of the appalling calamity in the room which is the body. The utmost source of terror to me was never the summons but this awful and yet *silly* moment, when the being tries to laugh it off, to leave it behind, to walk irresponsibly away. That ghastly moment is *funny* whether one can believe it or not. But have not many people written of the giggling silly horror of pure terror? Whether or not my last sensation, and the one I most dread, the one which has most nearly touched me with true neurosis, the one I cannot forget, is that laughter, that shrugging it off. The next instant I fall into nothing. This horrible light-hearted-ness and ghastly gaiety are not sensual—they are emotional. That is why they leave an impression which is ineffaceable, unforgettable and utterly fearful. I have had to battle with many a nervous rearrangement of the order of a fit: I have had many brief rehearsals which have made me cling to people, or if alone, to furniture or a task, to keep myself from fainting of fear. For when tired, overworked, over-wrought, worried or hurried as my brain is naturally apt to be, the feeling comes over me that I am going to begin to hover, and then to experience that dreaded second of irresponsibility. It has taken me months to train myself to be firm and to say reasonably: 'You are *not* going to have a fit because you are having the second symptom before the first,' and the order of a fit, as I have experienced it, is of a military precision. It never varies. An hysterical or nervous attack does alter. Or so I have been told.

The terror has without any doubt deeply affected me emotionally and mentally: I know how I am changed since I wrote *Autobiography*: I am more dependent on others, need more reassurance from ordinary people and though I hate company of the wrong kind, I am often most humbly glad of any. The world, the earth with its trees, plants, animals, its ores and rivers and seas is not less beautiful to me but is more blurred. It is not so much *myself* as it was. My soul has grown short-sighted. When in labour I was given a drug which separated me from my pangs without abating them. So have I been separated from my joys. There are times when they look back at me sad-eyed, as if in missing me they too were changing their immortal character. This, however, is not the place or the book in which to dilate on that theme. Here it is my wish to make myself concentrate on the description of those emotional shocks, and the very unhappy speculation they drew me into. And I find that in writing so hurriedly my thought is flung down like water upon a floor and dashed in all ways at once and wasted without channel. Of one thing I am beginning to be fairly sure, and that is that consciousness lags perceptibly, that it has powers of keeping, like certain foods, if placed in correct storage, that it will and *does* keep for years in some cases, so that the very essence which makes action, is old in us, old and far older than we may suspect or others guess. The consciousness which keeps us upright and even moving sensibly. My early discharges (as Professor T——calls them) were proved to be prolonged beyond the moment when any fresh current was being passed from my numbed brain into my mind. I have alluded elsewhere to the consciousness recording itself upon the mind; but a better illustration is provided by the thought of a spring where once I used to draw water, or to the basins of those descending fountains which flow into one another. The mind feeds from the brain as the first rock ledge was fed from the spring as it gushed clear and pure from the earth above it. The body or action feeds from the mind, as the water descended the second ledge into the sandy pool below where the bucket was dipped. The process therefore caused the loss of a fraction of time and a fraction of purity with each descent. Thus the pool would continue to be fresh and in movement for a short while after the spring had stopped spurting: and thus the body continues, I surmise, to contain a small supply of diluted consciousness after the mind and the brain have ceased their natural activity, and production of activity. If such a discrepancy in Time and quality exists between the brain and the mind, it must surely explain the behaviour of many insane people, as well as the recapitulation of a lifetime's existences in the dying?

There is astigmatism in vision as well as in sight. And memory is more likely to be vision than fact. Fact dissolves, but consciousness remains where fact put it, for moments, for days or for years. Fact and vision exist for all of us; and for all of us they must be as perfectly tuned into one stream as must be the separate sight of each of our physical, mortal eyes, to make one perfect sight. The visionary or mystic person, to which order of humanity belong many insane people, all dying ones, many epileptics and most young children, are consciously or unconsciously gifted with this habit of storage of impression or recapitulation. It is a split, a breach, an oddity between what should be a pair: and yet it can teach the healthy and the normal not *how* to think, but *what* to think. For disease goes very far towards Truth. The Mystic, the Psychic, and the Insane, come to us always with one story of a completion (completeness) which somehow is not sensed by the very ones whom one would suppose to be the natural people to perceive it—those who are in themselves a physical oneness, whose sight is tuned, whose brain is matched with mind, whose ears hear the same message on both sides of the head. From these people we learn little that is not material and wonderful, from the others nothing that is not vague and hopeful but is not wanted by the world in general. And yet from one of them, Isaiah, came the profoundest revelation of God-the-enigma ever written, the message which should soothe all religious controversy and spell peace among the doctrines and be cradle-song under the bitter meditations of all knowledge—halting all dogma:

> "For my thoughts are not your thoughts, neither
> are your ways my ways, saith the Lord" [1]

neither is there particularizing.

[1] Isaiah 55-8.

The mad are spell-bound by old consciousness, and new action or vice versa: the psychic speak of, and out of, 'trances,' children out of truth, mystics out of meditation, the dying out of life. And the epileptic partakes of all these dispositions—the mad, the mystic, the psychic, the childlike and the dying. And yet I think his disease is not a quality but a lack of quality. Either psychically, or spiritually or even religiously, he is hungry and he is not fed. He can speak to us at least of appetite; and his glimpses of the whole, the Oneness of God, may be as the thought of bread, pure and simple, to the hungry, who do not have visions in their extremity, of a diversity of deliciousness, but of one plain pure satisfaction and peace.

Never send thy thoughts for me,
I will stay in loneliness
living till all shadowless
droops on me Eternity.

When so patient, thou in bliss
and peace and sight shall gather me
to mingle in thy breast with thee
forgiving the abyss.

Never send thy voice from thee
nor let the seldom trumpet call
only when my hour befall,
only send thy heart for me.

CHAPTER III

RICHARD JEFFERIES was not in his living nature a mystic, but dying he became one, and wrote *The Story of My Heart*. He should have called it *The Story of My Tuberculosis*. For in its passion for life, though not in its content, it became mysticism. The mystic's intensest longing is not for life and health and beauty, as Jefferies', it is not for nature or natural life, though with that it begins as in Emily Brontë, it is for Death, that the breach may be closed, the completeness entered, the two sights made one. Thoreau, an economist, a dry philosopher, a student and a wit of wood life in a great and uninfested solitude, *was* a true mystic. He proves that the kind of person who is mystic (or psychic, as others prefer to call what they imagine is the same thing) is no more like a preconceived mystic than a poet is like a poetic personality. Thoreau possessed the dry precision, the scientific inspiration of the true mystic who is often most matter-of-fact in his ways of expression. What Jefferies was, was a *Romantic*. I use these two great men who died at about the same age of the same sickness, as examples for two reasons—the first is that the psychic personality is unrecognizable unless it confesses itself unconsciously to those who understand it better than itself, the second because they both belong to my encirclement by the images of the dead. Though Thoreau was nearer to me, and more interesting as a writer. He was a very great writer indeed—perhaps the greatest writer on natural life in the English tongue. Yet the longer part of his *Waldon* could be taken by normal people to be ordinary nature notes in very good prose. The same has been written of Herman Melville, the greatest nature writer of the sea, by one who passes as a critic.

The mystic and the psychic individual, although they are of the same mentality, differ in that the mystic is a religious entity who has visions (sometimes without any Vision) while the Psychic has physical experiences, and is not always or by any means religious. The mystic meditates or prays himself into vision—the psychic simply arrives there, often very startlingly, and without any warning.

The attacks of epilepsy both major and minor I have suffered seem to me to resemble the inexplicable arrival of certain experiences into my life from early childhood, or if one counts dreams, from infancy. I have seen what are called ghosts: they frighten me terribly, but they do not hold my attention in the same way as other experiences which seem, from what little I have read, to contain a curious resemblance to Yogiism. The first I can remember was not involuntary: it was fully conscious and it was self-willed. I was a child of nine when I learned to read and read the clock. I was prouder of being able to tell the time than of learning to read because it was not, although so late, so much a part of me. To read, once I could, was *myself*—to tell the time remained a proud and alien accomplishment. Sitting on a stool one day, at nine years old, in a room I shall never forget because it was home, I fixed my eyes on the clock. It was a cold clock, a 'dining-room' clock in the shape of a Grecian temple, made of what looked like black marble, and its face had a gilt rim. Its chime was low, abrupt and musical. I looked at it, and suddenly, for no reason, I said I would not breathe for five minutes while I watched it. *Neither did I.* At the end of the five minutes, I began as smoothly and quietly to breathe again as if I had never left off. A little while after, thinking of this experiment, I suddenly became inexplicably frightened of what I had discovered was possible and had done and I made up my mind and gave my word to myself that I would never do it again. Nor did I: but only a few weeks ago *the same thing happened involuntarily*. My breathing ceased: it dried up like a stream in summer. Some minutes later it came on again as before. There was no distress, no gasping, no oppression, but the same feeling of mental dread. Could I, I ask, have gone into an epileptic fit and thought I watched the clock move when I was a child when really all my eyes did was to pounce on the hand after an interval of gentle unconsciousness?

Another very sudden psychic experience was seeing the aura of a dog. This was only a few years ago. The dog was a black labrador, fat and glossy. I was walking into the village when suddenly he appeared with a bluish-lilac halo all round him in pure daylight. This time I was not frightened but as strangely delighted as I had been alarmed by my suspended breathing; and coming back from the shop, was disappointed to see the dog a plain black body again without his incandescent background.

One of my difficulties in writing this account, one that has encountered me progressively more and more power-fully since I began, is that the things I have written, more, even the mere words, appear to me continuously as questions to which I am unable to find any reply. Hitherto I have regarded writing a book or an essay, story or poem, as a kind of *statement* of something which exists either within or without the mind. But here I find no such continuous form; in fact I find no statement whatever except the flow of question. I am, therefore, not telling, but asking a story.

Having used both words, psychic and mystic, I have

looked them up in the dictionary, only to find that the word *spiritual* is entwined with both. It was not for my meaning that I searched the dictionary; but for others'. My own meaning is quite clear to me: a person may be, and probably is, both psychic and mystic, but he is not in those states of being at the same time. That I should like to emphasize: when in the psychic state one sees or hears something distinct from oneself, something apart, something odd and however usual to the seer, unusual to daily life. Such visions are, except when induced, inversions of what is expected. They may be the lining of the material world exposed when we did not so much as perceive it was torn.

When in the *mystic* state, in so far as I understand it, nothing is seen or heard, but what I have called the vision without vision (or without a seen picture) occupies, and in occupying dissolves, the senses in one certain sure understanding. Whatever the mystic experience, whether religious or coming from Nature or from the consummation of an art, one knowledge seems to be inseparable from the moment—the knowledge of union. To be in the mystic condition is to feel with mind, spirit and brain, Perfection, and not only Perfection but participation in it.

The psychic condition is to feel separate or distinct: the mystic, embraced. Those states which border on the mystic state are when Perfection is perceived but not quite assimilated.

How perceived, if neither heard nor seen? In conscious thought. Memorably so, so that a woman of my age can remember an experience near to mysticism in childhood.

I was ten years old. Dressed in a let down, faded, old green cotton dress with feather-stitching round the neck, with bare arms and legs of summer brown and feeling throughout every limb down to the ends of every finger and toe the delight of warmth, youth and unmaterial happiness, standing in a field, and saying to myself, or rather hearing myself say to me: 'This is the best time you'll ever have. Now you are perfect—ten years old.' And never telling any one, and knowing I was right. As most truly I was. This happened to me one year after the falls from the pony which are the only accidents I ever had that were at all likely to cause a scar on the brain. The first experience, when the breathing stopped and was quietly resumed when I wished, I number as psychic because then I was solated. The second with the dog was also psychic because the dog was the centre. But the third was mystic because there was an apprehension of perfection, though only a physical one.

The words psychic and mystic I have used in relation to myself perhaps without sufficient training or gifts to deserve either, except that they do appear to be synonymous with spirituality. A spirituality not necessarily good, possibly bad, and it might be dangerous, but which in its turn I associate with epilepsy. It happens that quite lately, while writing this present chapter, a state of surprised awareness, or psychicness has overtaken me. I have felt some things physically which I never have before: hot and cold currents in the open air while in Clystowe on the way to the neurological institute have passed through me giving me gentle shocks. Burningly hot places in furniture in rooms without fire or sun, which I have rested my hand on, but which of course left no visible mark on the polished surface. Indeed I hardly looked, hardly troubled to feel, so sure was I of the psychic cause, which was working in myself by paring away the substantiality of the mind.

'I'm trying to eat more,' I told the Professor after

travelling down to Clystowe with a ghost in the empty seat opposite.

'Oh why?' he asked—for I am plump and well.

'It makes you feel more solid.'

'Oh yes, well, it will do that.' And he smiled and asked no more. Yet nothing more was needed. I understood that I was understood, just as when I wept before him I knew that although no doubt with him tears were as common as nails to a carpenter, his lack of apparent sympathy or even *notice*, was in fact the one comprehension of all things that the great minded all own in their particular way. The substantiality of the mind—the materialism of the invisible consciousness, how fearful and how heavy it is in us. Clogged with it, the being works clumsily, like cold hands covered with chilblains on a bitter early morning! When in this generally prevalent private era of mere living instead of thinking with living, I am terribly reminded of *cold*.

The material mood, however genial, has a poor circulation; the spiritual, by contrast, is agile and glowing. And can rest in cold adversity because of its own inner heat and radiance. The material mood is not even exact: it is a clumsy and a groping tool. I believe that true *thought* can be physical, but not material, that is not self-seeking, not self-justifying. Thought as I understand it. How may I, one may ask, presume to use the word 'believe' who have no belief? I believe in belief as others have said and therefore believe in all things. That is why, under the protection of a friend's faith I felt as safe as if in the presence of Dr. Y—— or Professor T——.

Belief is not Creed. There exists to-day, I am told, among some, a philosophical creed that there are no thoughts which cannot be defined by words. To me that is to deny the essential nature of thought. That would appear to be the reason why God also has ceased to exist for those of this philosophy because 'my thoughts are not your thoughts, neither are your ways my ways.' Contrary to this 20th century creed is the most striking passage in *The Story of My Heart*, that revelation of physical mysticism, of which the workings are to be felt in some of Jefferies's other books, notably *Amaryllis at the Fair* and *Bevis*— where he imagines the possibility of thoughts that have never been thought before. And he does not mean material thoughts or thoughts on scientific or other discoveries, but abstract thought and divine meditation. This is the kind of thought that we hear *through* the words of great poetry. The kind of divine suggestiveness of which Wordsworth was master. The words of great poetry are indeed almost transparent. Poets have never lost the sense of the divine anonymousness; and this is their greatness and the reason why they can expand our minds beyond the medium which they use. This will always be, in spite of the fact that many of us would name the angels if we could, and try to fix the grammar of their intercourse.

A nameless grandeur fills the ancient world of the gods whose innermost secret, sacred appellations were concealed in their purest servants. The same power is in witchcraft, in insanity, in mysticism and in the attacks of epilepsy, so mysterious, so suggestive in their before and after effects. There are no words for it, or only approximate ones. But that is true of many experiences. Who can speak pain? Who pleasure? Who can utter love? People who are suffering agony inevitably groan: 'nobody knows what I'm bearing.' And this passionate and tortured cry of *nobody knows* is the only impression that emotion, or suffering, or delight succeeds in conveying.

Nobody knows it is true, because *nobody can tell*. It

would seem that this creed of Philosophy held by so many people to-day, is a language severed from physical experience, religion and idealism. That severance does not leave to it very much except itself. A Philosophy that excludes all those shades and tones of the human experience of being in love, in pain and in communion with God or God's world can be complete and useful only to those who are short of human stature. If I could, I would like to challenge one of these concrete thinkers to an attack of epilepsy. He would recant after it and would have to revoke all his vocabulary of thought. Language is demanded by epilepsy, as by poetry, that simply does not exist; and no amount of agility can create it any more than tight-rope walking or dancing can create wings. Language can, however, in the hands of a master, suggest that greater, wordless language within from which mental and spiritual discovery issues. It can suggest truths which are the more certain for being inarticulate. 'The soul consists of harmony,' wrote William Strode in his lovely *Song in Commendation of Music*.[1]

[1] *Song: In Commendation of Music* 1658.

When whispering strains do softly steal
with creeping passion through the heart,
and when at every touch we feel
our pulses beat; and bear a part;
when threads can make
a heart-string quake;
Philosophy
can scarce deny
the soul consists of harmony.

Oh, lull me, lull me, charming air,
my senses rocked with wonder sweet!
Like snow on wool thy fallings are,
soft, like a spirit are thy feet.
Grief who need fear
That hath an ear?
Down let him lie
and slumbering die,
and change his soul for harmony.

167

Neither is it to devalue language to write of its inadequacy while believing in its suggestive powers: for those who contend that it is capable of holding all that exists within and without the mind, usually prove by their style of writing that they know least how to make it go farthest. Words, like money, cannot buy everything; and those who are richest in them, like wealthy people, know their limitations while those who are poorest believe that what they do not possess can do miracles.

And music? How to express the thoughts of Beethoven and Bach and Mozart in words that would justify their divine genius? That their music is idea and thought is presumably acknowledged.

Only the highest poetry, the noblest music, can diffuse certain spiritual truths. Both do so by harmony and by the utterance of suggestion and mystery. For we are mystery, and harmony is union; and we are union.

I have described four fits. Each one was remembered by me through some image. And this image was in each case a domestic tool. One was a blue-banded milk jug, another a coal bucket, another a coffee percolator, and the last I described, the fit in hospital by a spoon swaddled in a bandage. I have always had a great liking for simple tools, and those things that were called machines before the word machine came to mean something with an engine in it. In its old sense a machine was something which extended human agility while more or less keeping pace with human action. Their quiet and even usage, their calm purpose, brought them great beauty and smoothness. The scythe, the wavy steel of the ploughshare—all agricultural machinery while the horse kept it alive—what could be more graceful and more suitable except man's own muscles? What combine harvester can replace the horse-drawn reaper with its paddle-wheel that seems to mill the yellow field? Or what is more like a limb in its bodily familiarity than the spade? The oar too, the thimble, the cradle that rocks—all these are as a peasantry among the new bright aristocracy of up-to-date machinery, but they are impregnated with human action which is unforgettable still. For when man moves the machine it is a part of his circulation as no engine which moves him can ever be. So the only homely and comfortable remembrances of these fits were the images they left of usual things embedded in their horror. I remembered the jug and the spoon, etc., as a dying woman I once knew remembered the cluck of a certain hen, and with her last words, told her family to search for the eggs in the hedge where the hen laid them. As long as I had these images and the attacks remained far enough apart for forgetfulness *and* memory to combine, each retained a kind of separate personality. This was endurable. Towards the spring of 1951, however, within two months of my child's birth, I had two in eight days. What was worse, neither contained a central image. The drugs were temporarily increased: my daughter was born on March 22nd quite normally, and three weeks after they were decreased again and the fits began to come upon me in a regular cycle of every 22nd day. The drugs were increased again, and a period of exhaustion, dread and mental confusion followed of great mystic excitement. I was nearer to neurosis than at any other time of my life: I was too weak to control my emotions or my reactions to the fear of the attacks themselves and the fear within them. And yet it was also a period of meditation, study and analysis. By which I do not mean that I was free to brood apart on my disease—for I was in fact extremely busy—but that the very frequency of the attacks and the mental prolongation of them from one to another, gave me an opportunity to study them continuously. My brain seemed to insist upon *my* finding some explanation for its own behaviour apart from any other opinion, even of the highest order. And though at first this cast me into a talkative and 'writertive' gloom which must have been nearly insufferable for those who had to endure it, I believe that it helped me to find a solution and that that solution has, partly at least, been my salvation.

About this time Professor T—— saw me again. I asked him whether all epileptics suffered as much mentally from their fits as I? And he replied no, that some *enjoyed* them. And had I read Dostoëffsky on his fits? I had not and have not and shall not yet.

He asked me had I any sexual pleasure from them? No, I had not. No orgasms? No. And what did I mean by *suffering*? The feeling that I was split into two or more entities at the moment before unconsciousness. And after them, what sensations if any? Only grief.

In his soft voice, he repeated after me: only grief. He did not ask what grief, and if he had I could not have told him.

Then I asked him, could my disease be caused by what people call 'nerves'? Was it a neurosis? His answer to this was a sharp rebuke. I was not to talk of neurosis: I was not to use a word which I did not understand. And what exactly did I mean by 'nerves'?

'Fancy. Imagination.'

'No, neither could account for your discharges. If you meant the physical nerves, yes certainly epilepsy is a disease of the nerves. But you are not neurotic, nor hysterical. You are not that kind of person. There is a cause for this disorder of your brain. The area affected is shown by the encephalogram.'

This conversation cleared much tangled ground for me. I felt that being a sane and sensible creature I could now search for myself; and I left the Institute in peace and with more courage, with the Professor's promise: 'Since you suffer so we must stop them as far as we can. I cannot stop them altogether because to do so I should have to drug you to such an extent that life would be unbearable. They will fire off occasionally. But it's not much. Be brave.'

Dr. Y—— increased the drugs and regulated their timing. In two months he had broken the cycle. I remember looking at him once as he got into his car and thinking that to me he was a miracle. The cycle was not abruptly broken: at first it extended a few days and then all at once the disease seemed to disappear in so far as the actual attacks formed it. It was, however, for months afterwards a mentally chaotic time for me because although a fit is almost impossible to describe accurately and imaginatively by the sufferer, there are so many things in every day life which keep reminding one of the condition. Particularly anything to do with *deceit*, with counting, or with dividing. With *deceit* because the mind tries to deceive you that you are not going to have a fit when you are: with *counting* because (to me) it seemed until very recently that there were *numbers* of entities in me during the moments before I fell and with *division* for the same reason.

I will try to give examples. If I had to write a letter in which I wished to convey to the understanding of the person I was writing it to, certain facts which nevertheless ought not to be put upon paper in case they should survive, the mere thought of such an attempt at deceitful trickery caused a pang of terror like the preliminary 'call' of a fit; and I was obliged to cower back into simplicity, and either not write the letter, or not mention the matter in it although it might seem at the moment important. Such involved statements while avoiding statements were common at the time and I believe I wrote hundreds of letters and destroyed as many.

In the same way I could not bear to count the ingredients of a recipe for a cake or a pudding. Again the pang would shoot to my heart and I would wait for those transfixed symptoms. When in the fury of restless impatience and lack of concentration which preceded the major attacks, and is now following them again, I saw any one look at a clock, I felt a great but controllable fear. If a clock stopped I longed to say 'don't wind it.' For it seemed to me that I was lying bound on the very rail track of Time which presently must catch me and kill me as the freight engine killed Anna Karenina. I was able to master this and even to start the stopped clock myself. But I have never mastered the horror of dividing things, although that is fading since the fits have become less frequent. Whether it was the roots of plants in the garden, or a matter of balancing weights, or hanging nappies equally on either side of the clothes prop so that the line did not sag (being very low) the effect was, and sometimes still is, the same. All this must sound fantastic. Nevertheless, fits are fantastic, and there was something in these frightened withdrawals from certain actions and thought-actions which went profoundly with the attacks themselves. Though not the cause of the epilepsy, they were the cause of the mental suffering that went with it. It was the cause of the suffering, the terror before, the sorrow after, that I set myself to analyze.

And though no doubt the attempt I am making to describe that half mazed but sensitive and conscientious series of solutions must sound absurd, I shall make it. For it was only when the attacks came more often that the disease began to stir in me some idea of its mystic and poetic potency. Up till the birth of my child I had taken it very practically, and looked upon it as an inconvenience and a possible danger only. It now seemed to me that it was a struggle between myself and a mysterious individuality. And that that Individuality was the Past. And I was the Present. And that far from meaning me harm, the disease was trying to tell me about myself. It was now that I began to suspect its spiritual (or ethical) origin. For it seemed a Force which was determined that my soul should avoid others; that it should be sent away from earth to pray and to repair, and that returning, it should remember nothing of its hermitage, but that nevertheless *it would be remembered* for it. After so many years of invisible appearance in the world, I had created a Power, however incomprehensible and ugly and humiliating. It was like poetry. It was like having another occupation.

The first conclusion I arrived at was very frightening. It was that I really contained two or more entities and that one was my neglected Genie or Muse, now turning on me as Apollo turned his rage upon his seer Cassandra. For I knew that I had betrayed my ideas for everyday life. I had had this knowledge in my brain for years—I had had my creative laziness on my conscience—and it was one of the reasons why I named my child after the accursed prophetess of Troy, whose white image had stolen nearer and nearer to me in my imaginative hierarchy. The first idea I formed then of the cause of my suffering was a very old and up-to-date one—Split Personality. I based it on the elucidation of that hovering moment when just before I fell in the fit, the light-hearted notion took me (as it always did) that there were so many people in me to choose from and so many rooms I could go into all at once that there must be immunity or sanctuary in one. Also that my always falling in a doorway, which was a fact, except for the two attacks I had in bed, was actual proof of a two-way life. (When I used the word 'hover' to a friend who saw me fall in a fit, she said that that was exactly the word for what my body did before it fell.)

But in excuse for my neglect of my writing, it must be admitted that I had always had to fight with what is my notion of human love and duty, having never made enough money to buy myself proxies for either. This struggle between two ardent convictions, enemies and thieves of each other, was enough to start a conflict and to account for my tormented feeling of Time overrunning my days and nights.

If I were a sufferer from split personality, my intermittent but lifelong 'visions' of unity were all delusions, and my belief in the Oneness of us all with the Oneness of God was only some physical contour of the brain. There remained, it seemed to me, only hardihood, isolation, madness. And here I must attempt to answer while I am about it a criticism which has been made of my writing before, and will be again if this MS. is published. It is the use by one who has no lighted truth and no picture of holiness, no actual visible revelation at all, of the term 'vision.'

My reply to this is that in the world of revelation as in the earth of sight, there is blindness. That one may enter or be projected into revelation with all the senses but that of the sense of sight open and that one returns with only *sensations* of having been placed before beauty and peace.

"Kelmaney had been she could not tell where,
and Kelmaney had seen what she could not declare."

Kilmaney's state of being would not convince a philosopher

nor yet many doctors. But I am not writing for philosophy, which too long has held a monopoly of thinking.

There are two words which to me would seem to be inseparable from the word 'vision' and neither of these stands for any one sense, such as sight, for instance. One is Pause—and the other Intensity. There are two contradictory passages from my own work to which I would wish to refer here: the first is in '*Creed*' where I wrote something in the short preface to the effect that no one has ever seen anything instantaneously, for such a sight would mean *pause*, which in nature does not exist: the other is in *Autobiography* where seven years later and therefore nearer to the full development of the epileptic tendency dormant in me, I wrote—'Vision which is only plain seeing and feeling, with intense joy . . .' to which belief I would adhere now, only it is not always joy that is added to the plain seeing and feeling, but grief also, and the feeling of age and passing. But there I was speaking of the Nature vision; and though the nature vision is always joyful, yet I have learned that to be one with Nature is to be a human being married to an immortal, whose immortal spirit partner, as one ages, cannot feel pity for pain and decline and finally death. It is the happiest and the saddest of lives.

That the reaction of the Nature mystic depends upon vigour to respond to the breath of plant, wild and instinctive, life is proved I think in the decline into bitterness of D. H. Lawrence as his youth waned: and the gradual sadness which replaced his joy in nature, in Richard Jefferies. These are two who were 'married to the immortal.' Where, however, the spiritual or philosophical response grows with the decline of the physical force as in a mystic, there is no such sense of loss. An example is Thoreau and another Emily Brontë, whose writings reveal the nature mystic becoming the spiritual. This I believe to be the true unarrested development.

But the pause and the intensity within vision or revelation may occur anywhere in any surroundings. Whatever the circumstance, whether one is gardening, thinking of something or looking at a face, an animal or a leaf—that sight or state of mind is *prolonged*, it seems, although afterwards it will have been found to have fitted into clock time. The sight, however casual (of the leaf, say, as personally I have never experienced it looking at a person), *is made to last*; and the memory, like sharp scissors is meanwhile cutting round that shape which the consciousness will retain forever, or for as long as it itself lasts. So in that yogi-like experience of childhood, a breath was made to last, for me, for five minutes. Vision is something truly very simple —a breath, a leaf, but lengthened. Perhaps so is Eternity, just time made to last.

> I didn't know I was a pilgrim—
> no one had come to tell—
> I'd passed no miracles on foot
> there was no warning bell.
> I heard no prayer, no dead man spoke,
> I passed no sacred sign:
> I didn't know I was a pilgrim
> until I touched the shrine.
> How was it no one said to me
> that time is called Eternity?
> How that I went with certainty
> where Time is called Eternity?

Many, many poets, writers and painters [1] have recorded

[1] See also Van Gogh, whose vision was of 'ordinary' things in a pause and intensified, as opposed to a painter like Le douanier Rousseau, who was a visionary.'

these moments of intensity, pause and learning, particularly Rossetti, who learned from sorrow that 'the woodspurge has a cup of three,' and appears not to have observed that he had learned revelation; and John Clare, the whole of whose very great poetic inspiration rested not upon his madness but upon his 'plain seeing and feeling.'

But I will now leave vision, hoping that my use of the term in my sense is now understood and go on with my attempts in the spring of 1951 to find the cause, not of my epilepsy which Professor T—— had told me was physical, but of my mental suffering under so peremptory a disease.

It was my conclusion at first that my divided sensations were due to what I can only describe as being several entities and that the split itself was the result of refusal to serve the artists' creative impulse as often or as devotedly as I could. In a state of great mental and spiritual depression I remained until the last fit but one that ever attacked me. Thinking of this attack which happened in the kitchen doorway with my eyes fixed on my husband's face, without stopping but with deliberate probing for days afterwards, I *did* succeed in remembering the actual sensations of the fit more presentably to the mind than ever before.

Every fit except two had happened in a doorway, I told myself. But this did not prove a double entity or a two-way symbolism of existence necessarily, as I had thought. Could it not symbolize, or be an attempt of the Ego, to be though one, in many places? I thought that it might. And then recapitulated the horrible hovering indecisive sensations in all their ridiculous helplessness. What *in fact* was passing through that part of my brain which could still feel, see and, in a way, think? Why had I that dream or remembered sight of myself under those symptoms, as my sister sometimes and then again as myself, so that I knew 'how to behave in a fit,' as one knows how to behave at a tea-party if one feels sick? If I were two people, who were they? How was I to become one being, one brain, one soul again? And if I could not, how was I ever to recover even with expert help and medical devotion? The knowledge that I was not one entity but several possibly, I have written how it horrified me and how in supposing it I lost all the vision of Unity which had been mine all my life. The answer to the questions could only lie in exact remembrance of the attacks; and to this most secretly I applied myself. I *must* remember.

Always the fits began with the Call as I was facing one way, and usually I fell the other. What was I trying to do? Always it seemed I tried to race the Disorder, or beguile it away, turn it, evade it, disguise or hide it. And always it ended in failure. *Social* failure? Sometimes it seemed so. It seemed a convention of behaviour violated, as one of health, when I finally lost control of action and then of consciousness. In Proust is a description of the death of Bergotte, a writer assumed to be great, of apoplexy. It reveals immense and exact imaginative power, for it reproduces in the dying man, who is at a public exhibition, the attempt of one trying to *pass off* a dreadful physical disaster. It is not that Bergotte is afraid for himself, because it does not occur to him that this is death which is on him; but that bewilderedly he is trying to behave himself normally under circumstances not understood by himself. My experience of epilepsy confirms the exactness of Proust's discovery. One thinks one has succeeded in conquering or disguising the attack at the very moment when one is dissolving under it: victory seems certain, and an irrational gaiety resulting from relief causes the smile to be felt which is really a facial distortion, the airy wave of the hand which is a stiff strangulated gesture, and the easy turn towards normality which is a stagger. The last consciousness is of conquest, of success. All this I gradually came to assess. The solution lay one way or another in that terrifying second when one of two things was happening to me: either the entities which had gained entrance into myself were saying they would divide me as a nation is divided to the victorious: or my incoherent conviction that it was possible to be where I was and be elsewhere at the same time was spiritually symbolical of the One which is everywhere and the everywhere which is one.

It was weeks before this last explanation occurred to me. I began to write this book: I was always waiting for another attack which might bring me more memory and so teach me whether my vision or assessment of life was true or untrue, but no other attack has ever followed. And far from arriving at anything but a question—the question of what the body is symbolizing during an epileptic fit—I am aware of not having succeeded even in describing the mental processes of an attack. Still less why the idea of dividing or balancing anything should cause an intellectual panic, *because there is a likeness*. Undoubtedly for a second or two there is a spreading of personality. Or should personality be pluralized? There is, then, a feeling of expansion *and* inclusion. If this does not contain my conscious 'visions' of a truth that holds ourselves and all in the universe, I do not know what it does contain. A fit seems to me to be exactly that illustration which my instinctive and untrained psychic and mystic moments never brought me. The peace has become unconscious; the union so much more profound than through the senses, that to leave it and return to life is to return through a backward looking and yearning sorrow in whose utterly incomprehensible bitterness I could never have believed. I repeat I would never have believed in such grief for I did not know that a sorrow without a conscious reason existed.

That a certain type of mysticism, spirituality or psychicness is a part of epilepsy I do believe even if the sufferer be mentally afflicted or I would not have written so much on this point. But the power is imperfect, which possibly begins the conflict, for only those who have it yearn for its perfecting. To those who believe in God and our part in God, it is imperative that He *must* exist: to those who stand a long way back and cannot reach believing, the hope is as much as God to the believer. Whereas to those who are unaware, there is no necessity and of course no conflict. That is why I ask, can epilepsy be a physical, unconscious awareness of a spiritual lack?

CHAPTER IV

December 30th 1951

THIS spiritual lack does not take the form of a hunger for any formal religion. It is the personality, not the presentation of God, that I long for. Equally sure am I that the term 'split personality' conveys no truth to me. It is not one being divided that causes the mental suffering and the physical collapse, but the presence within one brain, one body, one mind, of two or more *complete* entities. To use a simile of birth, the individual is not with child of Siamese twins but with unbound twins wrestling for the opening to life.

When I was much younger I kept a diary of my dreams and dream poems which I called 'The Diary of the Genie.' I think now it is a pity it was lost or destroyed. It might have given to me or to my physician the knowledge which I am seeking. The knowledge which I have not found and which it seems I shall not find.

Six weeks have passed since I last wrote in this book. Six weeks when I have written nothing. In that period I have ended the psychic phase, passed through a horror which I will describe, and finally entered that state of miserable impatience and mental velocity which tormented me for so many years before the great wave of the disease parted me perhaps forever from the land of normality (for my normal behaviour and calm appearance do not deceive me into thinking that I *am* normal). I have had another attack of epilepsy, possibly two, but considerably milder.

I have tried to explain how time has come to mean nothing fixed to me: in certain moods it seems I slip in and out of its meshes as a sardine through a herring net. Having once discovered periods of *action* which I could not remember, the trust which normal people rest in their own continuity has left me. I *knew* this, but a few days ago I *felt* it once more. There was no question of a fit: no time on the clock-face was lost, and had I not been alone the nightmare hallucination could not have occurred since one word from some one present could have reassured me. As an example of the terror and horror which can afflict such people as myself—whom I do not deny have superior joys also as compensation—I shall mention it.

It was one night last week. My husband had gone with a friend to see 'The Lavender Hill Mob.' The baby was in her cot upstairs asleep and I was in the living-room downstairs. Suddenly there was present in me the ghastly thought that, outside my consciousness, I had been active again, that I had mounted the stairs, gone into my baby's nursery, and killed her, and that I had only to go up once more to find her dead. It was useless to reason with this monstrous idea, to tell myself that all I had ever done unconsciously that could be called active was to get to my feet after a fit and reel a few yards up a country lane, blindly seeking the help that some part of me knew was there—the only thing was to go up and look. *The only thing*. The house was silent. I did it. I went up step by step until outside her door I heard her breathing! And the experience left no more mark upon me than one's guilt marks the clock-face at the indelible hour of a vile action. Indeed control is an almost fathomless state. For I have no doubt that had a late visitor arrived, as often happens, I should merely have said, 'How do you do,' and made a cup of tea. Yet my very reason sweated.

The very curious and peculiar dreams which often go before my nightmare periods have also begun again, as though I were working my way backwards through the symptoms which came to a climax in that first major attack in the cottage. How I hope it may be so! The very beauty in the detail of the background of these dreams fascinates me, even though the central activity is so pathetic or so sinister. The detail of tree-flowers, of a paisley pattern, for instance, in the dream last night, and the peace of the dying doll's smile. She began as an old woman, life size, but dumb, and my sister and I, children again, but with our adult life as memory between us, had to bury her. The scene was at my uncle's farm, at the bottom of the big lawn under the two great wych-elms now cut down. My sister told me that we must frill the shawl about the old woman's head, and then carry her and bury her in my aunt's flowers outside the greenhouse. The shawl was an old paisley shawl of mine. We took the body by the head and the feet and carried her the well-remembered way past the snow-ball bushes, over the sand path. Then we found the way barred by a tremendous growth of low-boughed trees. Sian said: 'This is what they have let grow since we were here.' 'This is the new way,' I said, 'look, Rosamund's footmarks, we have only to follow them.' As we skirted the trees I noticed the flowers hanging among the leaves—pale greenish white, sweet smelling—and I told myself they were lime-tree flowers, which they did not at all resemble, and that I must break off a spray and try to strike it, *because I should never be there again*. When we came to the greenhouse we laid the body down.

Without surprise I saw that she was no larger than a doll
and that she was not dead. Bending over her I looked into
her eyes and saw recognition.

'You are not dumb now?' I said.

'No,' the face said, just moving the lips.

'And it's all right?'

'Yes,' and smiling, the doll-woman died while blood
welled over her face. And with her smile the dream ended.
It left me with that strange feeling of accomplishment
that such dreams always have, almost as though the spirit
had put forth a movement as in the writing of a poem or
the translation of beauty into human terms. Whether the
little dead old woman who turned into a dying doll has
any significance only a psychologist can judge. For myself,
I am interested only in the connection between the details
of the dream and the reality of certain things. The paisley
shawl, for instance, is a real one, but more than that I had
been given as a Christmas present only two days before a
beautiful old Welsh quilt in a blood-red paisley material.
And the blood that welled over the face at the last moment
I saw when my spaniel bitch's puppy was killed six weeks
ago. It seems that dreams waste nothing. They are neither
the past nor the present, but a harmony of both such as
the waking memory cannot ever achieve. They contain
the reconciliation of all opposites, as when carrying the
dead woman my sister Sian and I appeared to each other
as the children we had been in that garden, and yet were
aware of the years which had passed over it and ourselves,
years that were made palpable and tactile in the growth
of the trees over the path.

I have little more to say that will not go into very brief
space, for the answer to my questions has never come to
me except by sensation, and of that interpretation who

could be sure? To me it appears as if Nature and creative art, meditation and religion, were God itself and that there is no separating the prayer from the answer, the accomplishment from the desire. Certainly from the records of the saints it seems sure that agony and doubt are inseparable from belief and joy: and that is why the writings of those who are passionate and humble worshippers of God are the best expressions of the souls of those who are non-believers. Belief experiences disbelief as disbelief never can, and the words of those for whom God does not exist are constant avowals of His presence—for when is light so expressed as at midnight, or darkness so clear as at noonday? The opposite of each thing makes the outline of the other; and the anguish and torment of the guilty is never so well said as in the annals of the innocent—for only the innocent can feel guilt.

I have felt that the causes of my disease are my fault more than my body's. It is true that wrong though my life has been and no doubt will be, I have never committed a major 'sin.' Yet do I know that? True also perhaps as many modern philosophers and ordinary thinkers tell us that there is no wrong-doing, but only mistaken doing. For a deed is so slight a thing at its doing and action grows not with action but with the passing of Time over it. It was so slight a thing perhaps, the thought of having done it marred not one day at the time. Yet later, from this same thoughtless cause every thinking day was wrecked and doomed from its dawn. I regard my life not knowing how to regard it and longing only for the verdict of an infinite intellect one way or another. What use is a 'conscience,' a mere another part of a consciousness to me, what help is an answer from the question? What answer could I accept from a human being, a priest, a doctor, an alienist, a poet even? None. For 'their thoughts are not my thoughts.'

If evil-doing exists—and I incline to the acceptance of it as fact—it seems to me that I can illustrate its beginnings and endings thus:

Supposing such a thing possible, you go out on an early autumn morning, the sun just risen, the light and shadows fresh, and a ghostly half substance, partly dew, partly cobweb stretching from stubble blade to stubble blade. You walk unhindered over the fields full of freedom and joy. This is youth. By the night time each impalpable silver thread is turned to iron chain—the fields and your feet are in fetters. This is age. This simile, unreal as it is, haunts me. The thought of the iron tie which is neither regret nor repentance, but simply the consequence of that which seemed so frail. I cannot rid myself of the vision of the iron cobwebs, nor that my spirit has indeed felt them. I see them where the world was lovely. This is the natural growth of mistakes. Repentance might break the chains, regret soften them. *But I feel neither.* I feel that I was deceived. Is this the lure? For Herbert writes that God lures us to His breast, and he if any man had insight into infinity. Why this ray of darkness on me while it is day? To teach me death? Compassion? That it has done and for that, if I have lived wrongly, to bring this disease, I would praise the disease, for to understand grief is beyond the understanding and the committing of art—even if a person's art is the only way he can think of God's self. There are two ways a person may live and be perfected. One is in his own spirit, the other in the necessities of others. I would put the latter lower, even now, for 'one thing only is necessary.'

A few years ago in our village a woman died who was

not young. She was discussed in her death as she had never been in her life, for in life she had been all but personally non-existent except as a third hand to every one of her family and connections. She had been so divided up among them as a piece of extra activity that as a woman, and a sick woman, she had scarcely been noticed. She died in a lane under a tree struggling in a snowstorm to reach the bus so that she might take one of her grandchildren to see the shops. For her heart was worn out. That was a happy woman. None could doubt it. She had never known a moment's useless pang. Her life and her death so moved me that I wrote a poem about her, for I thought hers had been one of the two spiritual perfectings.

An Old Countrywoman

Here is her body.
Mary who was given to John.
There are her hands
drowned in the buckets of water
with wrinkled nails
like shells in the sea:
These her arms
crucified on the red forest of the fire:
and her back
she gathered load by load
and bore
as Jesus bore his only tree.
These her eyes;
they saw God
in the necessities of others.

Her body shall sleep
she shall rest in the miles.

She shall not hear
the dry wood creak for the fire,
nor the cow low,
nor the clock stop,
nor the ripe fruit fall,
nor the garment tear.
She shall rest
for her feet are full of hills.

That is one perfection, as a human being can achieve it, to see God in the necessities of others. But it does not perhaps contain the perception of the necessities of God. And therefore the response to God. It is complete as a life story but contains no hint of a spiritual future. It is a perfection and an achievement which ends with the end of the mortal life, which travels to the grave and there rests.

The other Perfection which is not, I will say, scarcer, but rather more difficult to perceive since it seems egotistical, one is not able to describe very clearly since its consummation rests with the Unseen, the Unknowable and the Unproven. Only the smaller part of it is lived visibly by living persons. Like Emily Brontë, they would seem to step rapturously into the grave as into some mysterious incandescent spiritual activity and affinity with God rather than into the rest and peace which crowns the tired and selfless beings who have all their lives found in the wants of others their sacred and holy hill. This second way of Perfection leaves few monuments except in great art. Therefore it is not mourned. It is not the greatness of the humanity shown in the dead life which is wept for, but often its small humanisms. Of such mystics was the great Bach. For the interpretation of God is very often in this way of Perfection, its only living preoccupation and then not particularly a religious God but rather an inspiring one. The serenity in death of such holy people of genius is most natural, for their vigil is over. Like Bach and like Blake—a selfish and egotistical man in small ways—they die in the music of their own spirits.

But what if one is an ordinary, even if a disordered spirit? How can one achieve then either way of Perfection when one hardly understands why or how the idea of Perfection has entered one's life? I believe that one cannot. I know that I cannot. I can only choose which pattern of the two I would wish to attempt to follow, had I the continuity in me to wish for so long. And thinking on the two ways I would by instinct, hope and temperament choose to try to follow the second way. For if the first, the way of the old country woman, leads to rest, the second leads to immortal waking.

And I have not lived unless my errors have lived as me. And I, the child, have not woken, but my errors did, for me. And now less than ever when the drugs I have to take to prevent the discharges of the epilepsy make me apathetic, have faded and dulled and dimmed the powers of imagination and concentration. Restless but helpless, no action seems worth taking since the only true activity is born of serenity—

> "Lovely forms do flow
> from consent divinely framèd"[1]

And there is no profound satisfaction or harmony without it. Forms being actions—the only shapes thoughts can assume outside arts and prayers.

[1] Thomas Campion, *Rose Cheeked Laura Come.*

What to do with this dark, restless, pining life? I see now that the questions in my mind will never be answered, for my silent disease has no reply for me.

When I shut my eyes, in the voluntary darkness of my eyelids, I see the place I would wish to be in with my child, and yet I do not know whether it exists or whether I have made it. It seems to me I have been there, but if not it has been to me. It is very clear to me—a high, grassy common where the bracken grows and the sheep graze, among the branches of our Border hills. I even see the smoke of hidden cottage chimneys scattered among the windy trees. I reached it once when I was about sixteen, or thought I reached it: but I could never find it again. I remembered the village, the fields, the unusually long wood I passed through on the way; but although I have been all over that part of the country where it should be, it has vanished. It has simply disappeared. Either I got over a gate and fell asleep and dreamed it or large tracts of country can do this. But suddenly, the other morning, early awake in the dark, I saw it again and this time a fantastic certainty filled me that now I could inhabit it. And that that is what I should do. And that if this is the only thing I can find in me to want to do, it is the right thing. The only thing.

Resignation

Do not delude yourself your days will bring
one fairer than their dark-faced family;
your days are gipsies, but not bastardly
light have they bred outside their hovering
and swarthy circles. Yet they dance and sing
though sad; and chant with briony
and nightshade round their brows, to be
at least familiar in their cloudy entering.

And if a stranger-one appeared to you
brighter and softer, different voiced and quiet
as they are never, with its eyes of blue
fixed on your eyes, as if the sky shone throuş
its gaze you'd doubt it for a spirit
and turn from it, not knowing what to do.